Study Aids

Pygmalion

Bernard Shaw

Guide written by
Stewart Martin

Charles Letts & Co Ltd
London, Edinburgh & New York

First published 1988
by Charles Letts & Co Ltd
Diary House, Borough Road, London SE1 1DW

Illustrations: Betty Eberl and Peter McClure

This series of literature guides has been
conceived and developed by John Mahoney
and Stewart Martin.

The authors and publishers are grateful to
The Society of Authors on behalf of the
Bernard Shaw Estate for permission to quote from
Pygmalion, published by Penguin Books Ltd.

Stewart Martin is an Honours graduate of Lancaster University, where he read English
and Sociology. He has worked both in the UK and abroad as a teacher, an educational
consultant and a writer. He is married with three children, and is currently Deputy
Headteacher at Ossett School in West Yorkshire.

John Mahoney has taught English for twenty years. He has been head of English
department in three schools and has wide experience of preparing students at all levels
for most examination boards. He has worked both in the UK and North America
producing educational books and computer software on English language and literature.
He is married with three children and lives in Worcestershire.

British Library Cataloguing in Publication Data
Martin, Stewart
    Pygmalion: Bernard Shaw: guide.—
    (Guides to literature).
    1. Drama in English. Shaw, Bernard.
    Pygmalion – Study outlines
    I. Title   II. Shaw, Bernard, 1856–1950
    III. Series 822'.912

ISBN 0 85097 847 5

Printed and bound in Great Britain by
Charles Letts (Scotland) Ltd

Contents

To the student

This study companion to your English literature text acts as a guide to the novel or play being studied. It suggests ways in which you can explore content and context, and focuses your attention on those matters which will lead to an understanding of, and an appreciative and sensitive response to, the work of literature being studied.

Whilst this guide covers all those aspects dealt with in the traditional-style study aid, it is, more importantly, a flexible companion to study, enabling you to organize the patterns of study and priorities which reflect your particular needs at any given moment.

Whilst in many places descriptive, it is never prescriptive, always encouraging a sensitive personal response to a work of literature, rather than the shallow repetition of others' opinions. Such objectives have always been those of the good teacher, and have always assisted the student to gain high grades in GCSE examinations in English literature. These same factors are also relevant to students who are doing coursework in English literature for the purposes of continuous assessment.

The major part of this guide is the 'Commentary' where you will find a detailed commentary and analysis of all the important things you should know and study for your examination. There is also a section giving practical help on how to study a set text, write the type of essay that will gain high marks, prepare coursework and a guide to sitting examinations.

Used sensibly, this guide will be invaluable in your studies and help ensure your success in the course.

George Bernard Shaw

'Mr Shaw is a writer of comedy with a tragic cry in his soul. In the Middle Ages he would have been a great saint, appalled at the gracelessness of men's hearts, militant for the Kingdom of God. Today he is a playwright, appalled at the muddle-headedness of his race, a fighter for the conquest of reason over unreason, of order over disorder, of economy over waste.'

Ludwig Lewisohn, 1915

George Bernard Shaw was born in Dublin on 26 July 1856. He became the most controversial and provocative writer of the first half of the 20th century, the 'upstart son of a downstart father'. His education was rather patchy, although he inherited a love of the arts, especially music, from his mother. He developed and retained a powerful thirst for knowledge.

In 1876 he left Ireland for ever and went to London to join his mother, (who had left her alcoholic husband) and tried to earn a living writing novels, short pieces for magazines, and drama and music criticisms. Many of the latter were extremely perceptive, although he had all five of the novels he wrote between 1879 and 1883 turned down by publishers. In his early years in London, before he became famous for writing plays of his own, he struggled to make a living and had to be supported by his mother.

This led to his remark: 'I did not throw myself into the struggle for life: I threw my mother into it.' He became deeply influenced by the ideas of Karl Marx, and eventually became a powerful public speaker and committed socialist. From his political and economic opinions grew his vision of society as a broken-down organism which badly needed change and repair.

Shaw's first play, *Widower's Houses*, exposed the evils of wicked landlords and slum housing. In 1898 he followed this with *Mrs Warren's Profession*, which was a biting attack on upper-class hypocrisy and the underlying causes of prostitution. *Major Barbara*, in 1905, attacked the notion that charity removed squalor and poverty. His other plays dealt with 'social' themes such as the futility of war, the stupidity of heroism and the failure of modern politics.

In a letter to Ellen Terry on 8 September 1912, Shaw mentions that he had in mind to write a play for Forbes Robertson and Mrs Patrick Campbell (two famous actors of the day) 'in which he shall be a West End gentleman and she an East End dona in an apron and three orange and red ostrich feathers'. This is the play which, fifteen years later, was completed as *Pygmalion* in June 1912. In this play Shaw attacks the notion that differences of class or social status are to do with important human characteristics – instead he says they are mostly matters of money and superficial things. We can see his effective use of characterization in *Pygmalion* and the way he used and developed contemporary social issues in his themes, such as social class, wealth and status. Shaw's themes were, in fact, so successful that the stage plays were sometimes turned into films. *Pygmalion* was turned into *My Fair Lady* and the text of the stage play had some scenes added by Shaw specifically for the cinema version.

Shaw was a very versatile dramatist, a social thinker, a writer and a master of comedy. His ideas invariably caused surprise in their frequent inconsistency and the fact that they would often ricochet from one extreme to the other. He was, however, always consistent in the way he avoided what was pompous, condescending or over-serious, and his plays often achieve powerful effects through his skilful use of humour. Exactly how great a dramatist he was is still a matter which causes some argument amongst scholars; for his own part, Shaw ranked himself about number ten among English playwrights.

George Bernard Shaw won the Nobel Prize for Literature in 1925 and died in 1950.

Table: Character presence chart — *Pygmalion* (Act 3: Mrs Higgins's house; Act 4: As for Act 2; Act 5: As for Act 3)

| | | Mrs Higgins's house | | | | | | | | | | | As for Act 2 | | | | As for Act 3 | | | | |
| | | 3 | | | | | | | | | | | 4 | | | | 5 | | | | |
9	10	1	2	3	4	5	6	7	8	9	10	11	1	2	3	4	1	2	3	4	5
Eliza returns from her bath, transformed	Eliza has a speech lesson	Higgins arrives unexpectedly	Mrs and Miss Eynsford Hill arrive	Pickering arrives	Freddy arrives	Eliza arrives	Eliza leaves	The Eynsford Hills leave	Higgins and Pickering discuss the experiment	The Embassy reception	The hostess meets Eliza	Nepommuck identifies Eliza as a princess	Higgins and Pickering discuss the reception	Pickering goes to bed	Higgins goes to bed	Eliza leaves	Higgins and Pickering arrive	Mr Doolittle arrives	Eliza enters	Eliza meets her father	Mrs Higgins, Doolittle and Pickering leave
●																	●	●		●	●
								●	●				●			●			●		
●	●	●		●	●	●		●		●		●	●	●		●	●	●	●	●	●
	●	●	●	●	●			●	●	●			●	●	●	●		●	●	●	●
						●	●														
				●	●	●										●					●
			●	●	●																
		●						●											●		●
								●													
										●		●									
●						●			●				●	●		●	●	●	●	●	●
	●					●		●	●					●		●	●	●	●	●	●
		●				●		●						●		●		●	●	●	●
●		●		●	●	●	●	●		●	●		●					●	●	●	●
		●				●								●		●	●	●	●	●	●
		●				●		●	●				●	●		●	●	●	●	●	●
		●	●			●				●	●	●	●	●		●	●	●	●	●	●
	●					●								●	●	●		●	●		●
35	36	38	39	39	39	39	40	40	41	41	42	42	44	45	47	47	50	50	52	53	54

Finding your way around the commentary

Each page of the commentary gives the following information:

1   A quotation from the start of each line on which a comment is made so that you can easily locate the right place in your text. (Remember to read around the exact reference to get the sense of the context.)

2   A series of comments, explaining, interpreting, and drawing your attention to important incidents, characters and aspects of the text.

3   For each comment, headings to indicate the important characters, themes, and ideas dealt with in the comment.

4   For each heading, a note of the comment numbers in this guide where the previous or next comment dealing with that heading occurred.

Thus you can use this commentary section in a number of ways.

1   Turn to that part of the commentary dealing with the act you are perhaps revising for a class discussion or essay. Read through the comments in sequence, referring all the time to the text, which you should have open before you. The comments will direct your attention to all the important things of which you should take note.

2   Take a character or topic from the list on page 22. Note the comment number next to it. Turn to that comment in this guide, where you will find the first of a number of comments on your chosen topic. Study it, and the appropriate part of your text to which it will direct you. Note the comment number in this guide where the next comment for your topic occurs and turn to it when you are ready. Thus, you can follow one topic right through your text. If you have an essay to write on a particular character or theme just follow the path through this guide and you will soon find everything you need to know!

3   A list of relevant relationships between certain topics will be found on page 22. To find these in the guide turn to the comment indicated. As the previous and next comments are printed at the side of each page in the commentary, it is a simple matter to flick through the pages to find the previous or next occurrence of the relationship in which you are interested.

For example, you want to examine in depth the character of Mrs Eynsford Hill. Turning to the character list, you will find that she is first discussed in comment 16. On turning to comment 16 you will discover a zero (0) in the place of the previous reference (because this is the first time that she has been discussed) and the number 43 for the next reference. You now turn to comment 43 and find that the previous comment number is 16 (from where you have just been looking) and that the next reference is to comment 45, and so on throughout the text.

You also wish to consider the relationship between love and money throughout the play. From the relationships list, you are directed to comment 35. This is the first time that both love and money are discussed together. You will now discover that two different comment numbers are given for the subject under examination – numbers 41 and 37. This is because each topic is considered separately as well as together and you will have to continue tracing them separately until you come to comment 42 – the next occasion on which both love and money are discussed.

Comment number

Quote from play

Previous appearance in guide

Character or idea under discussion

8 'Nah then, Freddy: look wh' y' gowin, deah.'
One of the sources of comedy in the play is Eliza's absurd cockney accent, which Shaw is at pains to stress. This is why he repeats Eliza's penetrating cries and her 'I'm a good girl, I am.'

6/15   Stereotypes
7/9   Eliza

Next appearance in guide

Commentary

Topics	Comment no:	Characters	Comment no:
Class	16	Colonel Pickering	1
Freedom	2	Eliza Doolittle	1
Love	3	Henry Higgins	1
Mannerisms	15	Mrs Pearce	1
Money	9	Alfred Doolittle	1
Slavery	2	Mrs Higgins	4
Stereotypes	1	Mrs Eynsford Hill	16
Violence	2	Clara Eynsford Hill	2
		Freddy Eynsford Hill	2
		Nepommuck	58

Almost all of the characters exist in interesting relationships with the themes in the play. Below are some of the interesting relationships which exist between themes:

Relationships			Comment no:
Love	and	Freedom	48
	and	Slavery	35
	and	Money	35
	and	Violence	29
Slavery	and	Freedom	2
	and	Money	9
	and	Violence	2
Class	and	Stereotypes	18

Commentary

Act Two

Act 2

1 Eliza arrives, unannounced, for lessons
21 'Good enough for yǝ-oo.'
Eliza has come for lessons. The two men are stunned. Notice carefully how a few lines further on Eliza gives her reasons for wanting lessons. These are an important link throughout the play.

19/25	Class
17/23	Pickering
20/25	Eliza
17/22	Higgins

22 'Oh, I know whats right.'
This is the first of the occasions in the play when Higgins rattles the money in his pockets. He always does this when he is trying to avoid getting involved with things which disturb his peace of mind; his 'off-the-cuff', nonchalant air is a device to hide this. The rattling of coins here also indicates the underlying basis of the relationship between Higgins and Eliza. Think about this more carefully – consider Higgins's offers of sweets, taxis, and so on – who is bribing whom here? Or, to put it more basically, who is buying whom here?

9/35	Money
20/26	Slavery
21/23	Higgins

The role of money in the play is complex; sometimes its possession is seen as a means to enjoyment, sometimes as a great burden – Doolittle, for example, moves from being in one relationship with it to the other. The Eynsford Hills are a contrasting example to Doolittle in this regard. But is the scene here an occasion where Higgins uses money to eventually enslave Eliza? Later on we see how Doolittle and Mrs Pearce both press Higgins directly on this matter, as do Pickering and Mrs Higgins a little more indirectly. Indeed, we see how the question is raised as to whether Higgins has 'bought' Eliza for sexual pleasure. Would you say that Higgins is taking advantage of Eliza here? If not, what is he doing, and how does the use of money in the scene reflect this?

23 'Higgins: Im interested. What about the ambassador's . . . ?'
When talking about the proposal to pass Eliza off as a lady, Pickering uses the word 'experiment' to describe the project; later on in this scene he does so again. Does this word seem shocking when used in this way about the life of a human being? It does not seem to shock either Pickering or Higgins here. This is interesting, because it does shock Pickering later on in Act 5. Why could this be, do you think?

21/32	Pickering
22/24	Higgins

2 Pickering and Higgins make the bet
24 'What is life but a series of inspired follies?'
How effectively do you think this sums up Higgins? What does it tell us about Higgins's attitude to such things as responsibility?

23/25	Higgins

25 'Yes: in six months – in three . . .'
Higgins says that within six months, possibly three, he could teach Eliza to speak in such a way that he could take her anywhere and 'pass her off as anything'. This is Shaw's key point about the way society is divided: class distinctions are artificial and can be overcome in six months by anyone who studies phonetics. Shaw had in mind, when writing *Pygmalion*, to produce a play which demonstrated to the public both the value of phonetics (in which he was deeply interested) and the absurdity of class. He wished to illustrate the sadness of the fact that the way a person speaks seems to have a lot to do with material success or failure in life, and with how they are treated. Eliza latches onto this last point at the end of the play, and realizes that 'The

21/31	Class
16/27	Mannerisms
18/32	Stereotypes
21/27	Eliza
24/26	Higgins

difference between a flower girl and a duchess is not how she behaves, but how she is treated.'

---

3 Mrs Pearce protests about the situation
26 'You must be reasonable, Mr Higgins . . .'
In spite of Mrs Pearce's protests Higgins goes ahead with his plans. Later in the play Eliza comments that Higgins can twist women around with his charm, and we see a good example of this in his next speech: *'I* walk over everybody!'

22/28	Slavery
25/27	Higgins
1/31	Mrs Pearce

---

27 'I'm going away. He's off his chump . . .'
This is a very trying interview for Eliza, who is insulted, bullied and coaxed in turn by Higgins. Given that Higgins make things so difficult for her, why does she not actually get up and leave, as she threatens to? This is a key episode to understanding Eliza, for it gives us an insight into her determination and ambition. Throughout the rest of the play it becomes clear that Eliza's lessons from Higgins are painful things for her, and it is largely on account of her own hard work that the 'experiment' is eventually successful.

Although Eliza does not have the benefit of Higgins's formal education, she is obviously quick-witted and intelligent. She also has a very strong character which, in spite of Higgins's boorishness and arrogance, remains unbroken to the end. Not only does Eliza fling criticism back at Higgins, she eventually flings other things also – like slippers! One of the things which keeps Eliza going through her ordeal, as Shaw makes plain in the sequel to the play, is her ambition to become a lady in a flower shop. Would you say that it is her ambition which keeps her going, or the feelings of affection which she develops for Higgins?

20/28	Freedom
25/34	Mannerisms
25/28	Eliza
26/28	Higgins

---

28 'Very well, then, what on earth . . .'
Higgins makes the staggering assumption here that because Eliza has no mother and has been turned out of her home, she 'doesnt belong to anybody'. He then assumes that she is of no use to anybody but him. Why does it never occur to Higgins that Eliza may belong to *herself*? Does he think of her as a person at all?

27/30	Freedom
26/35	Slavery
27/29	Eliza
27/29	Higgins

---

29 'Oh, youve no feeling heart in you: . . .'
Compare this with Eliza's comment to Higgins at the end of Act 5 – how accurate was her first impression here?

3/32	Love
13/30	Violence
28/30	Eliza
28/30	Higgins

---

30 'Youre a great bully, you are.'
It is only when Eliza refuses to let Higgins bully her any more that she becomes truly 'free' to become herself. Notice that bullying is a sign of immaturity in people, the sort of behaviour which is normally associated with children.

28/37	Freedom
29/31	Violence
29/31	Eliza
29/32	Higgins

---

4 Eliza is taken for a bath
31 'I cant. I wont. I'm not used to it.'
The episode of Eliza's bath is both funny and sad in what it reveals about her background. Mrs Pearce is not above being stern with Eliza, even though

25/37	Class
30/33	Violence

she is also kindly towards her. It is clear that Mrs Pearce feels sorry for the girl, but this does not stop her from forcing Eliza to do as Mrs Pearce wishes: 'Eliza's screams are heartrending.'

5 Higgins and Pickering discuss women
32 'Excuse the straight question, Higgins.'
Pickering wants to know whether Henry is 'a man of good character where women are concerned'. Pickering's question, and Higgins's reply, are important because of the important relationship which develops between Eliza, Higgins and Pickering. But the matter is important in another way, because although the background of the play is to do with phonetics the play is essentially about human relationships and especially about love, as the title suggests. Even though Shaw suspected that the story and outcome of the play would be thought extraordinary, he nonetheless subtitled it 'A Romance in Five Acts'.

Unlike most of Shaw's other plays, the preface to *Pygmalion* is remarkably short: Shaw felt that the play should speak for itself. However, the ending of the play caused so much interest (misunderstanding, Shaw might have said) that he felt it necessary to write a sequel, almost as though the play was incomplete. In a way, of course, it is incomplete, but that was Shaw's intention. Do you think that he should have written a 'happy ending'? How do you feel about Shaw's view that to do this would have spoiled the whole point of the play? Your views on this will, of course, be coloured by how much you consider the play to be a 'Romance'.

6 Mrs Pearce criticizes Higgins's habits
33 'I swear! . . . I never swear.'
In spite of all his wealth, his education, his years and his size, Higgins is much like an overgrown baby who, as his mother remarks in the next act, needs continual watching in order to keep him out of mischief. Mrs Pearce here begins just such a watchful telling-off of Higgins, which Pickering finds extremely amusing. In this respect Mrs Pearce is not only a sort of mother-figure to Higgins, she also acts as his nanny. Note all the characteristics which contribute to Higgins's infantile streak: he has tantrums, he sulks, he has no table manners, he leaves his clothes scattered all around the house, he throws Eliza's ring into the grate, he swears violently when he does not get his own way and lays hands on Eliza when she says she might join Nepommuck and teach phonetics.

Given that Higgins has so many distasteful sides to him, why is it that in spite of ourselves we rather like him? Shaw suggests that it is because he has no conscious malice in him – that he is 'incorrigible' (that is, beyond all hope of correction). Certainly Higgins seems a difficult person to socialize with, although he and Pickering seem to get on well together – why might this be? How much of their relationship is founded on the fact that they are both shy, middle-aged bachelors, passionately interested in only a very narrow slice of life – in phonetics?

7 Alfred Doolittle arrives
34 'Have you no morals, man?'
This famous line, and Doolittle's even more famous reply – 'Cant afford them, Governor' – sum up much of the theme of the play. Not only can Doolittle not afford morals, he does not want them, for he enjoys not having morals. Does Doolittle play unscrupulously upon the feelings of others do you think? Consider how far his attitude is a very convenient façade, behind which he can play the con-man.

remarks? How has she 'hit' him, and why does he say he is 'wounded . . . to the heart'?

Imagine how Higgins must look on stage, with the jewellery hanging out of his pockets. Apart from appearing rather ridiculous, might he remind us of some common house-burglar, and if so, what has he really stolen from Eliza?

3 Higgins goes to bed
81 'Damn Mrs Pearce; and damn the coffee; . . .'
When driven beyond patience Higgins lapses into swearing, ranting and shouting. He tries to be dignified but Shaw tells us that he spoils his exit by 'slamming the door savagely'. In other words he has a tantrum.

4 Eliza leaves
82 'Goodnight, darling, . . .'
Freddy's farewell is repetitive and sentimental, just like his affection for Eliza. This scene, excluded from the stage-play but present in the film, illustrates the bond between Eliza and Freddy and prepares the way for the drama's ending. Their love is simple and sexless, and contrasts strongly with the complex and stormy relationship between Eliza and Higgins.

Does the love between Eliza and Freddy seem juvenile to you? Does it seem to you that the Eliza we see here is the same Eliza who has just bested Higgins in a blazing row?

83 'Now then! . . .'
The elderly policeman arrives. He is a symbol of authority, a parent figure who tells them off for being naughty. The lovers flee from him to seek their freedom.

84 'He didnt half give me a fright, . . .'
Eliza slips easily back into her old pattern of speech. Presumably she feels that as Freddy does not regard her as the 'heartless guttersnipe' which Higgins does, she does not need to maintain any defence against him and can be 'herself'.

This raises a quite interesting question at this point in the play – exactly who is Eliza now? A guttersnipe, a flower-girl, or a lady?

85 'To make a hole in it.'
Eliza has contemplated suicide. Whether this remark is made partly to gain Freddy's increased sympathy is difficult to tell. If serious, Eliza's comment shows how far she was prepared to go to escape from her enslavement.

86 'Now then, you two! . . .'
The appearance of a second policeman is an almost exact repeat of the first. By this device of simple repetition Shaw makes the scene lighthearted and amusing. But notice the menacing overtones in Eliza's comment: 'It's their business to hunt girls off the streets.' This is another reference to the theme of prostitution and slavery which runs through the play, and is a skilful

reminder on Shaw's part that we have just witnessed the breaking of one bond of enslavement and are now seeing the forging of another. But who is enslaving whom here?

87 'Can I drive you and the lady . . . ?'
This is a beautiful echo of the start of the play when, after bumping into each other, Eliza and Freddy's meeting was effected through a taxi. Given Eliza's lifelong passion about taxis the rest of this scene is very appropriate – Eliza's fate seems to be determined by taxi cabs!

Notice how Shaw very subtly reintroduces the theme of money. Why might he want to do this? (Consider the previous comment in this Guide).

Although it was Higgins who first bought Eliza for £5, it is Pickering's money which allowed the 'experiment' to proceed. It is also Pickering's money which allows the action of the play to continue here and which provides support for Eliza even beyond the end of the play. To see how important it is that it is Pickering's money which is involved, think about whether the whole effect would have been different if it had been Higgins's money Eliza uses here and during the rest of the play.

84/88	Freedom
86/96	Love
80/88	Money
70/100	Pickering
86/88	Eliza
81/95	Higgins
86/117	Freddy

Act Five

Act 5

1 Higgins and Pickering arrive

88 'Eliza's bolted.'

Higgins's main concern at the loss of Eliza is that he 'cant find anything'! He says that he doesn't know what appointments he has or where to find anything. He talks about her as though she were an animal he owned – horses 'bolt' – and informs the police of her loss, treating her, as Mrs Higgins notes angrily, as though she were 'a lost umbrella, or something'. Notice how he wants to know if Pickering has offered a reward. How upset do you think Higgins is at the loss of Eliza as a person? Do you suspect, from anything which he says, that he values her for herself and that all this fuss is because he really is upset? If this is correct, why should he go to such lengths to deliberately conceal his human feelings for Eliza? Higgins's attitude may not be as straightforward as it seems – remember that he is talking in front of his mother. Could this have any effect on how he speaks of Eliza?

89 'Doolittle! Do you mean the dustman?'

Pickering immediately thinks of Doolittle in terms of his job as a dustman. This makes for an extremely effective contrast when Doolittle actually enters, 'resplendently dressed', and is a clever piece of stagecraft on Shaw's part. The effect on stage is impressive.

2 Mr Doolittle arrives

90 'See here! Do you see this?'

Doolittle has come up in the world and blames Higgins for it. The amusement in this scene derives from the fact that what had happened to Doolittle would be regarded as overwhelming good fortune by most people. To Doolittle it is a disaster – he has been delivered into the hands of 'middle class morality' as he puts it a little later.

91 'Ah! You may well call it a silly joke.'

This is very clever writing. Doolittle points out that what Higgins thought was a joke was taken seriously by others. There is a telling parallel here between this and the manner in which Higgins took up the 'experiment' with Eliza – as a 'folly'. The other clever reversal here is that Shaw takes Doolittle's new-found station in life and, whilst laughing at the 'joke' of it, makes us see the serious side.

92 'It aint the lecturing I mind.'

Doolittle's comic effect is enhanced here not only by his amazing transformation from dustman to 'toff', but also by his speeches. Shaw used this device often: making characters speak in a way which they would never have done in 'real life'. We saw in Act 2 how Doolittle could debate morality with the best of them, and here he proceeds to 'lecture' the others.

This illustrates neatly one of Shaw's purposes in his playwriting. In 1909 Shaw give evidence before a Parliamentary Committee on censorship and, although the Committee refused to take it into account, he began his evidence with the following words, which tell us a lot about why he wrote his plays: 'My reputation has been gained by my persistent struggle to force the public to reconsider its morals. In particular, I regard much current

Characters and ideas *previous/next comment*	
87/91	Freedom
87/90	Money
87/95	Eliza
84/90	Class
86/93	Stereotypes
38/90	Doolittle
89/93	Class
88/94	Money
86/91	Slavery
89/91	Doolittle
88/93	Freedom
90/93	Slavery
90/92	Doolittle
69/96	Mannerisms
91/93	Doolittle

morality as to economic and sexual relations as disastrously wrong; . . . I write plays with the deliberate object of converting the nation to my opinions in these matters.'

93 'That's the tragedy of it, maam.'

Doolittle's words do not seem to 'fit' the dustman character, even less this dustman who has come up in the world. These longer speeches here work much less well than the amusing conversations of Act 2, because they assume the 'lecturing' tone that Doolittle seems to adopt. How far do you think that Shaw has actually used Doolittle as a mouthpiece for his own opinions?

90/96	Class
91/100	Freedom
91/94	Slavery
89/96	Stereotypes
92/97	Doolittle

If Doolittle is a mouthpiece he is an eloquent one and, ironically, this is a parallel between him and Eliza. Just as Eliza has been made into a live 'doll', a kind of clockwork 'lady', so Doolittle seems to have become something of a ventriloquist's dummy, a 'live doll' just like his daughter. Notice how Shaw, by keeping the sentences short, ensures that the audience's attention does not wander during these long speeches.

The reference by Doolittle in this speech to 'the Skilly of the workhouse and the Char Bydis of the middle class' is both appropriate and amusing. The reference is, in fact, to Scylla and Charybdis. In classical mythology Scylla was a well-known dangerous rock in the Straits of Messina (off the coast of Italy) which sailors had to avoid. Near the opposite shore was another danger, the powerful whirlpool of Charybdis. When trying to sail through the Straits of Messina, sailors had to try to avoid the one without perishing because of the other. A modern equivalent might be to be 'between the devil and the deep-blue sea'.

Doolittle's reference is amusing not only because it applies to him and many other characters in the play, but also because it is spoken by the dustman, not the professor with the 'Miltonic mind'. As always in *Pygmalion*, Doolittle turns the world upside down!

94 'Well, you took that money for the girl; . . .'

Higgins says that Eliza 'doesnt belong to' Doolittle, but to him. He seems blind to the staggering irony in his accusation that Doolittle is either 'an honest man or a rogue'! In order to have come out with such a remark, Higgins must be still thinking of and regarding Eliza as 'property'.

90/98	Money
93/104	Slavery

95 'Just the other way about.'

How accurate is Higgins's account of the events of the previous night? What conclusions can you draw from his comments that Eliza threw the slippers at him without his giving her 'the slightest provocation' and 'the moment I entered the room – before I had uttered a word'?

85/103	Violence
88/100	Eliza
87/99	Higgins

96 'I think I know pretty well . . .'

Mrs Higgins knows her son well and is an astute judge of character. Also, Mrs Higgins has just told everyone that Eliza is upstairs. It seems certain that she will have talked the whole incident over with Eliza. Is Higgins actually lying here, or can we believe that he still does not realize what he did? But notice how Mrs Higgins, too, falls into the trap of judging people according to their class – she says that Higgins simply does not realize 'what anything in the nature of brain work means to a girl of her class'.

93/97	Class
87/98	Love
92/99	Mannerisms
93/97	Stereotypes
55/120	Mrs Higgins

97 'Now, now, Enry Iggins!'
Doolittle has just heard Higgins tell Pickering to behave in front of Eliza, 'this creature that we picked out of the mud' as Higgins calls her. Now Doolittle remonstrates with Higgins and tells him to consider his feelings as 'a middle class man'. The humour here lies in the fact that, given the way Doolittle himself has treated Eliza in the past, his concern is ironic to say the least. Also, Doolittle is playing the part of 'middle class man' – last time we met him he was playing the part of 'undeserving poor'.

96/102	Class
96/102	Stereotypes
93/98	Doolittle

98 'As you wish, lady.'
Doolittle, whether or not 'middle class man', is still anxious to keep Eliza off his hands. Now that he has plenty of money why should this be so? Why is he so determined to evade his responsibilities as her father?

96/100	Love
94/101	Money
97/106	Doolittle

99 'I am behaving myself perfectly.'
Higgins's comment is amusing because it is preposterous – Higgins does not know how to behave himself. Pickering's reply emphasizes this – 'He is doing his best, Mrs Higgins' – and immediately Higgins demonstrates what his 'best' is when he 'throws back his head; stretches out his legs; and begins to whistle.' The irony of Higgins the scientist, the man of learning, who is an expert in speech and manners behaving the way he does throughout the play, is a rich source of humour and social comment.

96/103	Mannerisms
95/103	Higgins

3 Eliza enters
100 'Will you drop me altogether . . .?'
Pickering says he is shocked to hear Eliza call her experiences an 'experiment', but at the start of Act 2 he was perfectly happy to use the word himself. Why do you think that he has changed his mind and now feels uncomfortable at Eliza's use of the word? What has changed in the time between the two incidents?

93/102	Freedom
98/101	Love
87/101	Pickering
95/101	Eliza

101 'It's not because you paid for my dresses.'
Eliza explains for the benefit of the audience the debt she owes to Pickering – both financial and moral. Is it a much greater debt than the one she owes to Higgins?

100/104	Love
98/106	Money
100/0	Pickering
100/104	Eliza

102 'Oh, thats only his way, you know.'
In defending Higgins, Pickering voices one of the play's themes – that whilst Higgins should be forgiven for his misdemeanours because he 'doesnt mean it', nobody extends an equal licence to flower girls: 'But you see I did it; and thats what makes the difference after all.'

97/105	Class
100/104	Freedom
97/107	Stereotypes

103 'I know. I am not blaming him.'
The comedy in this speech by Eliza, in which she exposes Higgins's attitude to others for what it is, is emphasized by the way Shaw has Mrs Higgins criticize him for grinding his teeth immediately after Eliza finishes talking. It comes as no surprise when, a few lines further on, Higgins explodes!

99/105	Mannerisms
95/111	Violence
99/105	Higgins

104 'Forgive! Will she, by George!'
Higgins still has not realized that Eliza is more than just a beautiful creature who has been taught to speak exquisitely. Here we find Higgins saying that Eliza will be unable to manage without him and Pickering: 'She will relapse into the gutter in three weeks without me at her elbow.' But Eliza's outlook on life is now more important than her way of talking, and later on in this act we see her turn her back on her teacher. Throughout the play Higgins has treated Eliza as a speech phenomenon, a beautiful talking doll, or a laboratory experiment – he has constantly ignored her as a person.

It is possible to see that, in fact, Higgins does not really change Eliza at all. What Higgins does do is to change one stereotype (the flower girl) into another (the fashionable lady) and that it is actually Eliza's resentment at being treated as some kind of experiment which leads to her explosion in Act 4, and that, finally, it is *this* which leads to her transformation.

102/108	Freedom
101/106	Love
94/109	Slavery
101/105	Eliza

4 Eliza meets her father
105 'No: not now. Never again.'
Eliza says she could 'not utter one of the old sounds if I tried'. The comic effect here is made all the greater because it is well signalled in advance. We know what will happen when Eliza sees Doolittle, and we are all the more amused to be proved right: 'A-a-a-a-ah-ow-ooh!' Higgins is beside himself in victory: 'He throws himself on the divan, folding his arms, and spraddling arrogantly.'

Shaw deliberately varies the kind of humour he uses, so as to retain the freshness of the action. Witty 'one-liners' are interspersed with irony, outrageous lies, sarcasm, laboured good manners and farcical stage business. This carefully written scene is an excellent example of craftsmanship.

102/106	Class
103/0	Mannerisms
104/107	Eliza
103/110	Higgins

106 'You must have touched a millionaire . . .'
This is the climax of Doolittle's story in the play. Dressed like a millionaire, he is going off to be married. It is an interesting ending for Doolittle, if only because it is probably what he, and the audience, expected to happen to Eliza rather than to him. Shaw has written the subplot of the play as a kind of reversed story of the main action. Apart from the fact that this makes the play more interesting to us, can you think of other reasons why Shaw might have done this? Consider what kind of conclusions you think we, the audience, might be expected to draw from the story of Doolittle. What, for example, do we conclude about the corrupting power of money? And what about Doolittle's comment earlier in the play about how a lot of money would make him unhappy – was he right?

105/107	Class
104/108	Love
101/125	Money
98/108	Doolittle

107 'If the Colonel says I must, . . .'
Eliza is not without her own snobbery. Is she reluctant to go to the church because she thinks she will be 'insulted', or because she does not want to meet 'that low common woman'?

106/120	Class
102/108	Stereotypes
105/113	Eliza

108 'I feel uncommon nervous . . .'
Once again Doolittle takes us by surprise. Pickering assumes that Doolittle has been married before and will therefore be familiar with the procedure. When it is clear that he has jumped to the wrong conclusion, Pickering becomes flustered. This is another illustration of how quickly and easily people make assumptions and thereby categorize others.

104/111	Freedom
106/111	Love
107/110	Stereotypes
106/109	Doolittle

109 'Do stay with us, Eliza'
With this remark the stage is cleared of all actors but Eliza and Higgins, and the drama moves to its climax. Notice the clever way Shaw uses Doolittle's wedding to achieve this effect of isolating the central characters. This is a good example of Shaw's dramatic technique.

104/113	Slavery
108/120	Doolittle

5 Mrs Higgins, Doolittle and Pickering leave
110 'Without accepting the comparison . . .'
Higgins reveals a more kindly side to his nature now that he and Eliza are alone together. How far does Higgins's explanation of 'the great secret' justify his behaviour towards her and others in the play? Does Higgins have 'the same manner for all souls'? Compare him to Pickering in this respect.

108/114	Stereotypes
105/111	Higgins

111 'So you are a motor bus: . . .'
How apt a summing up of Higgins's character is this metaphor? And how true do you think is Eliza's taunt to him: 'I can do without you: dont think I cant'? Who is Eliza trying hardest to convince – Higgins or herself?

108/113	Freedom
108/112	Love
103/122	Violence
110/112	Higgins

112 'I can do without anybody.'
Higgins makes what is obviously a false statement here. Compare this with what he said to his mother when telling her at the start of this act that Eliza had 'bolted'. As with the previous comment, who is Higgins trying hardest to convince – himself or Eliza?

111/113	Love
111/114	Higgins

113 'Well, you have both of them . . .'
This is the most crucial conversation in the whole play, for it is here that the truth is finally told. The distinction is made very clear between the surface appeal of Eliza as a perfect 'mechanical doll' and the more powerful attraction of Eliza the person with her own 'spark of divine fire'. Higgins accepts that 'the voice and the face' are not Eliza. He acknowledges that these are not the things which he will miss – he will instead miss her 'soul'.

Look carefully at the reply Eliza gives to Higgins's honest admission here of his feelings for her. Why does she say that, in spite of what he says, she thinks that he does not really care for her?

111/116	Freedom
112/114	Love
109/114	Slavery
107/115	Eliza

114 'I have never sneered in my life.'
Is Higgins correct here? What about his comments at the start of Act 4? This long speech is another of Shaw's 'messages', like those of Doolittle earlier in this act.

Higgins says he will not trade in affection, which is another reference to the theme of prostitution in the play. But he also says that he cannot be bribed by Eliza's fetching and carrying for him either. He rejects both kinds of slavery. Higgins makes the point that if people behave like slaves they will be treated like them, and must not then complain if others do not care for them. This reveals Eliza's pathway to freedom from the prison of her self-imposed slavery.

To what extent does Higgins's speech here contradict his actions elsewhere in the play, or is he consistent throughout the drama?

113/115	Love
113/116	Slavery
110/117	Stereotypes
112/122	Higgins

115 'I'm no preacher: I dont notice things . . .'

Earlier on in this scene, Eliza said that she did not mind how Higgins treated her and would not even mind a black eye, but that she would not be 'passed over'. Here we see again her concern about herself: 'I notice that you dont notice me.' Although Eliza is generally shown in a very sympathetic light in this act, Shaw does not neglect to reveal her more selfish side also. Think about her relationship with Freddy, her attitude towards her father's marriage to her stepmother, and her reasons for embarking upon the 'experiment' in the first place. How far do you think that Eliza is just as self-centred as Higgins, but in a different way?

114/117	Love
113/116	Eliza

116 'Oh! If I only could go back . . .'

How much of Eliza's pain is caused by her feeling that she really is a slave now who has genuinely lost all her independence? This is, of course, the same argument as Doolittle has recently used. To what extent is her pain caused by the breaking of her self-imposed bonds of slavery? Are her feelings of being exposed and vulnerable a result of the fact that in reality she is now finally free but is not yet used to the feeling?

113/119	Freedom
114/118	Slavery
115/117	Eliza

117 'Damn his impudence!'

Why is Higgins so upset that Freddy writes to Eliza three times a day and apparently loves her? If he is not himself interested, in a romantic sense, in Eliza why should he care? Do you think that Higgins is jealous?

A little later on in this scene Higgins says that he is interested only in the higher things in life, not in 'the life of the gutter'. He admits that his life is full of 'coldness' which makes him seem 'selfish' and 'unfeeling'. Although Higgins goes to great lengths to portray himself as an unemotional academic, do you find yourself wholly convinced of this? Do you think Eliza is completely convinced by his words? Do you even suspect that Higgins himself is unconvinced by his own arguments?

115/118	Love
114/118	Stereotypes
116/119	Eliza
87/0	Freddy

118 'Can he make anything of you?'

As Eliza promptly explains, that is precisely not the point, and this is where she and Higgins disagree most fundamentally. All she wants is to be 'natural' she says. Is what Eliza wants attainable, or is she being ridiculously sentimental?

117/119	Love
116/119	Slavery
117/121	Stereotypes

119 'No I dont. Thats not the sort of feeling . . .'

Although Eliza says here that she could have 'dragged' Higgins down to make love to her, she did not. Is it because she thinks too highly of him, or is it that she does not think enough of Higgins to want him to make love to her? Certainly Shaw felt this, as he says in the sequel to the play: 'Galatea never does quite like Pygmalion: his relation to her is too godlike to be altogether agreeable.' There are many other such examples in the sequel, but whilst it is clear that this is what Shaw thought, it has to be admitted that many since have seen it otherwise. You will need to make up your own mind about the relationship between Higgins and Eliza, and you must be in a position to support your views by reference to *specific points in the text*.

116/121	Freedom
118/120	Love
118/121	Slavery
117/120	Eliza

chair by the hearth. Pickering hesitates about following suit and Higgins tells him to throw their coats over the bannisters into the hall. Pickering collects them and goes downstairs. Higgins wonders aloud where his slippers are and Eliza gives him a dark look before going to fetch them. Pickering and Higgins begin to discuss the day. Eliza has apparently conducted herself impressively and although both men admit this, Higgins declares that he is glad it is all over and that he has found it all a terrible bore. Pickering has evidently found it all rather exciting, but declares that he was frightened on one or two occasions because Eliza was doing so well. Pickering admires Eliza's performance because it was so professional and congratulates Higgins on his achievement. So far neither of them has addressed a single word to Eliza, who has not spoken. Just as Higgins leaves, Eliza's expression becomes 'murderous', and we can understand why. Presumably Higgins and Pickering have ignored Eliza like this all evening, treating her like an object rather than a person. Higgins's over-the-shoulder comment to her to put the lights out is the last straw.

He returns to the lounge to get his slippers, just as Eliza's temper breaks, and she flings them in his face. Higgins is astounded and asks her why she did it. She tells him that she has won his bet for him and now she supposes he will throw her back in the gutter again. When Higgins reacts coolly to her outburst she tries to claw his face but he grabs her wrists and throws her into the easy chair. She asks what will become of her and Higgins says that he neither knows nor cares.

Higgins does not understand why Eliza is not glad it is all over, because she is now free. But of course she is not free, and Higgins cannot see that she is now like Mrs Eynsford Hill, fitted for nothing, with nowhere to go. Higgins still cannot understand, and says he had not realized she was going away.

(Extra scene – cinema version)
Eliza is packing while, outside her window, Freddy gazes up at her. As Eliza comes out of the front door, Freddy asks her not to laugh at him but says that he spends most of his nights there. They embrace, but an elderly policeman who is passing is scandalized by this behaviour. The lovers run away.

Freddy and Eliza arrive in Cavendish Square, where Freddy asks Eliza where she was going. She replies that she was going to the river to throw herself in it. Freddy is horrified and asks her what the matter is; Eliza says that everything is all right now, because they have each other. They embrace again and this time are interrupted by a younger constable. They run away again and find themselves in Hanover Square.

As Eliza and Freddy embrace for a third time, a passing taxi appears. They take the taxi to Wimbledon Common, determined to drive about all night. Eliza says that in the morning she will call upon Mrs Higgins.

Act 5

Mrs Higgins is writing at her desk when the parlourmaid arrives to announce that Higgins and Pickering are downstairs, the former being in something of 'a state'. Unknown to both of them, Eliza is upstairs, and Mrs Higgins asks the maid to tell her about the visitors, and to warn her to stay upstairs until sent for.

Higgins bursts in and tells his mother that Eliza has gone. Pickering, who has been telephoning, arrives and Mrs Higgins is scandalized to learn that they have sent the police looking for Eliza. In the middle of this the maid returns to say that Mr Doolittle is downstairs, having been sent on from Wimpole Street. When asked by Higgins whether he is a dustman, the maid replies that he is a gentleman. Higgins expects some 'genteel' relative but the person who enters is the Mr Doolittle we have already met – except that he is resplendently dressed as a bridegroom.

Doolittle blames Higgins for his new-found wealth and explains that he would not have minded if this fate had simply happened to him, but he is cross that Higgins seemed to have arranged it (however unwittingly). In answer to Mrs Higgins's queries he explains that Higgins wrote to a rich man in America who was setting up Moral Reform Societies around the world. Higgins praised Doolittle as an original thinker. The rich man, Ezra D Wannafeller, died and left Doolittle a legacy worth three thousand pounds a year. This huge sum of money is to be paid annually for as long as Doolittle gives lectures for the Wannafeller Moral Reform World League, up to six times a year. Doolittle argues that by doing this Higgins has ruined him, destroyed his happiness and delivered him into the hands of middle-class morality.

As Doolittle is obviously unhappy with his wealth, Mrs Higgins points out that he does not have to accept the money. Doolittle says that this is the tragedy of it, for who can refuse such wealth? Mrs Higgins is pleased that he can now provide for Eliza, but Higgins interrupts to point out that Eliza belongs to him, not Doolittle, because he paid five pounds for her.

Doolittle steps out onto the balcony as Eliza is summoned down to meet Higgins. When she arrives she is 'self-possessed' and gives 'a staggeringly convincing exhibition of ease of manner'. By contrast we see Higgins becoming increasingly exasperated as the scene progresses. Higgins instructs Eliza to return home, which she declines to do, and displays his poor manners. Eliza rubs salt in the wounds she is inflicting on Higgins by being very gracious and considerate towards Pickering, who she says has always treated her like a lady. Eliza says that Higgins, on the other hand, has always treated her like a flower girl. Just as Eliza says that she could never go back to her old self and her old speech now, her father approaches her, unseen, from behind. Her reaction upon seeing him is a high point of comedy as she reverts instantly to her old manner of speaking. Higgins is delighted, for he feels that this shows that Eliza's 'old' self is still there beneath the surface.

Eliza's 'new' self also includes snobbery, and she is cross that her father will be marrying her stepmother whom she describes as 'that low common woman'. Pickering points out that Doolittle ought to marry her and that Eliza should support him, rather than be critical. Eliza decides to go to the wedding.

As Eliza leaves to get ready, Pickering is asked by Doolittle to attend the wedding also, to lend moral support. Pickering expresses surprise at Doolittle's nervousness because he assumes that he has been through it all before. Doolittle's surprises are not over, however, and he announces that he has not been married before. Eliza does not know that she is illegitimate, and Pickering agrees not to tell her. He begs Eliza not to leave him and Higgins, but to stay with them in Wimpole Street, after which he goes with Doolittle to get ready for church. Higgins asks if Eliza has not had enough of her own back by now; her refusal to return puzzles him, until she explains that it is not being treated like a flower girl which she cannot bear, it is being passed over and ignored. When Higgins says that he will not be diverted from his path by anyone, Eliza replies that she can do without him. She says she will not care for anybody who does not care for her, and Higgins replies that all he can offer her is 'good fellowship'. Eliza is concerned about Higgins's never noticing the real 'her', but he can see only the challenge of the intellectual life and invites her to return to this 'for the fun of it'. He even offers to adopt her as his daughter and settle money on her in his will; he wonders whether she might marry Pickering. This enrages Eliza and she reveals how Freddy feels for her. In reply to Higgins's jibe that Freddy will never make anything of her, she points out that *she* may make something of *him*.

Eliza makes it clear that she could have trapped Higgins if she had wanted to, but that she has played fair with him. All she wants is a little kindness. Higgins seems to understand that Eliza cannot go back to her old life, but seems to assume that she must therefore go back to Wimpole Street because there is nowhere else to go. Eliza says that this is where he is wrong – she could marry Freddy or go and work for Nepommuck. Both these suggestions enrage Higgins and for the second time he forgets himself and loses his temper. She has finally found a way to get the better of him and presses her advantage – she will offer her services to Nepommuck, using the knowledge Higgins has given her to teach others how to be a duchess. Higgins is thunderstruck, but impressed in spite of himself by her impudence and courage; he likes her like this.

As Pickering returns to collect everyone for the wedding party, Eliza becomes cool and composed again. As she sweeps majestically out she remarks that she cannot imagine how Higgins is going to manage without her. As the play ends we see Higgins roaring with laughter at the prospect of Freddy's being married to Eliza.

Coursework and preparing for the examination

If you wish to gain a certificate in English literature then there is no substitute for studying the text/s on which you are to be examined. If you cannot be bothered to do that, then neither this guide nor any other will be of use to you.

Here we give advice on studying the text, writing a good essay, producing coursework, and sitting the examination. However, if you meet problems you should ask your teacher for help.

Studying the text

No, not just read – study. You must read your text at least twice. Do not dismiss it if you find a first reading difficult or uninteresting. Approach the text with an open mind and you will often find a second reading more enjoyable. When you become a more experienced reader enjoyment usually follows from a close study of the text, when you begin to appreciate both what the author is saying and the skill with which it is said.

Having read the text, you must now study it. We restrict our remarks here to novels and plays, though much of what is said can also be applied to poetry.

1 You will know in full detail all the major incidents in your text, **why**, **where** and **when** they happen, **who** is involved, **what** leads up to them and what follows.

2 You must show that you have an **understanding of the story**, the **characters**, and the **main ideas** which the author is exploring.

3 In a play you must know what happens in each act, and more specifically the organization of the scene structure – how one follows from and builds upon another. Dialogue in both plays and novels is crucial. You must have a detailed knowledge of the major dialogues and soliloquies and the part they play in the development of plot, and the development and drawing of character.

4 When you write about a novel you will not normally be expected to quote or to refer to specific lines but references to incidents and characters must be given, and they must be accurate and specific.

5 In writing about a play you will be expected both to paraphrase dialogue and quote specific lines, always provided, of course, that they are actually contributing something to your essay!

To gain full marks in coursework and/or in an examination you will also be expected to show your own reaction to, and appreciation of, the text studied. The teacher or examiner always welcomes those essays which demonstrate the student's own thoughtful response to the text. Indeed, questions often specify such a requirement, so do parmicipyte iw those classroom discussions, the debates, class dramatizations of all or selected parts of your text, and the many other activities which enable a class to share and grow in their understanding and feeling for literature.

Making notes
A half-hearted reading of your text, or watching the 'film of the book' will not give you the necessary knowledge to meet the above demands.

As you study the text jot down sequences of events; quotations of note; which events precede and follow the part you are studying; the characters involved; what the part being studied contributes to the plot and your understanding of character and ideas.

Write single words, phrases and short sentences which can be quickly reviewed and which will help you to gain a clear picture of the incident being studied. Make your notes neat and orderly, with headings to indicate chapter, scene, page, incident, character, etc, so that you can quickly find the relevant notes or part of the text when revising.

Writing the essay

Good essays are like good books, in miniature; they are thought about, planned, logically structured, paragraphed, have a clearly defined pattern and development of thought, and are presented clearly – and with neat writing! All of this will be to no avail if the tools you use, i.e. words, and the skill with which you put them together to form your sentences and paragraphs are severely limited.

How good is your general and literary vocabulary? Do you understand and can you make appropriate use of such terms as 'soliloquy', 'character', 'plot', 'mood', 'dramatically effective', 'comedy', 'allusion', 'humour', 'imagery', 'irony', 'paradox', 'anti-climax', 'tragedy'? These are all words which examiners have commented on as being misunderstood by students.

Do you understand 'metaphor', 'simile', 'alliteration'? Can you say what their effect is on you, the reader, and how they enable the author to express himself more effectively than by the use of a different literary device? If you cannot, you are employing your time ineffectively by using them.

You are writing an English literature essay and your writing should be literate and appropriate. Slang, colloquialisms and careless use of words are not tolerated in such essays.

Essays for coursework
The exact number of essays you will have to produce and their length will vary; it depends upon the requirements of the examination board whose course you are following, and whether you will be judged solely on coursework or on a mixture of coursework and examination.

As a guide, however your course is structured, you will be required to provide a folder containing at least ten essays, and from that folder approximately five will be selected for moderation purposes. Of those essays, one will normally have been done in class-time under conditions similar to those of an examination. The essays must cover the complete range of course requirements and be the unaided work of the student. One board specifies that these pieces of continuous writing should be a minimum of 400 words long, and another, a minimum of 500 words long. Ensure that you know what is required for your course, and do not aim for the minimum amount – write a full essay then prune it down if necessary.

Do take care over the presentation of your final folder of coursework. There are many devices on the market which will enable you to bind your work neatly, and in such a way that you can easily insert new pieces. Include a 'Contents' page and a front and back cover to keep your work clean. Ring binders are unsuitable items to hand in for **final** assessment purposes as they are much too bulky.

What sort of coursework essays will you be set? All boards lay down criteria similar to the following for the range of student response to literature that the coursework must cover.

Work must demonstrate that the student:

1 shows an understanding not only of surface meaning but also of a deeper awareness of themes and attitudes;

2 recognizes and appreciates ways in which authors use language;

3 recognizes and appreciates ways in which writers achieve their effects, particularly in how the work is structured and in its characterization;

4 can write imaginatively in exploring and developing ideas so as to communicate a sensitive and informed personal response to what is read.

Much of what is said in the section **'Writing essays in an examination'** (below) is relevant here, but for coursework essays you have the advantage of plenty of time to prepare your work – so take advantage of it.

There is no substitute for arguing, discussing and talking about a question on a particular text or theme. Your teacher should give you plenty of opportunity for this in the classroom. Listening to what others say about a subject often opens up for you new ways to look at and respond to it. The same can be said for reading about a topic. Be careful not to copy down slavishly what others say and write. Jot down notes then go away and think about what you have heard, read and written. Make more notes of your own and then start to clarify your own thoughts, feelings and emotions on the subject about which you are writing. Most students make the mistake of doing their coursework essays in a rush – you have time so use it.

Take a great deal of care in planning your work. From all your notes, write a rough draft and then start the task of really perfecting it.

1 Look at your arrangement of paragraphs, is there a logical development of thought or argument? Do the paragraphs need rearranging in order? Does the first or last sentence of any paragraph need redrafting in order to provide a sensible link with the preceding or next paragraph?

2 Look at the pattern of sentences within each paragraph. Are your thoughts and ideas clearly developed and expressed? Have you used any quotations, paraphrases, or references to incidents to support your opinions and ideas? Are those references relevant and apt, or just 'padding'?

3 Look at the words you have used. Try to avoid repeating words in close proximity one to another. Are the words you have used to comment on the text being studied the most appropriate and effective, or just the first ones you thought of?

4 Check your spelling and punctuation.

5 Now write a final draft, the quality of which should reflect the above considerations.

Writing essays in an examination
Read the question. Identify the key words and phrases. Write them down, and as they are dealt with in your essay plan, tick them off.

Plan your essay. Spend about five minutes jotting down ideas; organize your thoughts and ideas into a logical and developing order – a structure is essential to the production of a good essay. Remember, brief, essential notes only!

Write your essay
How long should it be? There is no magic length. What you must do is answer the question set, fully and sensitively in the time allowed. You will probably have about forty minutes to answer an essay question, and within that time you should produce an essay between roughly 350 and 500 words in length. Very short answers will not do justice to the question, very long answers will probably contain much irrelevant information and waste time that should be spent on the next answer.

How much quotation? Use only that which is apt and contributes to the clarity and quality of your answer. No examiner will be impressed by 'padding'.

What will the examiners be looking for in an essay?
1 An answer to the question set, and not a prepared answer to another, albeit slightly similar question done in class.

2 A well-planned, logically structured and paragraphed essay with a beginning, middle and end.

Love
&
London

Ellie White

CHAPTER ONE

Year's Eve is a wonderful tradition, a time for
time to dream of what's to come. For me? Well,
hat my Mum is here to hold my hand tight while
oom full of people listening to the overly
DJ that counts us down to midnight.

r has passed and, in 7 seconds, another year
a time where people all around the world
will not keep; pay for gym memberships
ttempt to give up alcohol for the month of
lves feel charitable. They'll fight over who
display. Sydney? Hong Kong? NYC?
ondon does it best, Edinburgh, a close

al. Nothing has changed for me. I'm
Year's Eve as last year and the year
before that. I know exactly how this
s with just getting through tonight.

Love & London

Please be aware that this book discusses death and grief. Includes mild swear words and scenes of an adult nature.

This novel is a work of fiction. Names, characters, places and incidents are either the product of the authors imagination or are used fictitiously. Any resemblance to actual persons, living or dead, business establishments, events or localities is entirely coincidental.

ISBN: 9798597564722
Imprint: Independently published
First Edition

For many, New
reflection and a
I'm just thankful t
we stand in a r
enthusiastic radio
10, 9, 8...
Another yea
begins. New Year is
make resolutions the
they will not use and a
January to make thems
had the best firework
Everyone knows that L
second.

7, 6, 5...
Here I am, as usu
reliving the exact same Ne
before that and many more
year will play out and it start
4, 3, 2...

The clock strikes midnight and everyone around me kisses and hugs each other, erupting in laughter and cheers, yelling 'Happy New Year' at the top of their drunken voices followed by the explosion of party poppers and air horns. As much as I don't want to, I make the effort to join in, for my Mum's sake. Just like every New Year, I give mum and dad a kiss on their cheeks before they start making their way around the room, embracing aunties, uncles, friends and neighbours.

One of the things I hate about New Year is the unnecessary touching. Don't get me wrong, I like a brief hug every now and then but having people I've not seen for 6 months want to hug and kiss me seems like overkill.

Like I said, it's the same every year. The same old people telling the same old stories. Janice from next door tries to set me up with her perpetually single son who she promises is a lovely man. Considering his first wife left him over his addiction to prostitutes and his second wife left him when he gambled away their life savings, I think I'll pass. Thanks anyway!

My Great Auntie Tricia talks enthusiastically about how innovative silent fireworks are. Little does she know, her daughter has turned down her hearing aids to preserve what is left of her hearing.

"Keep that chin up, you're doing great, kid," Ray, my dad's business partner and my boss, says as he claps me on the shoulder. He knows I hate these things but he also knows how important tonight is for my family.

Ray and I are like two peas in a pod; driven and meticulous, some may even say picky. We love a plan, a to-do list and to be in control. Our similarities are why I'm the Director of Strategy at his and dad's advertising agency, Sixth Street Advertising. My attitude towards our work is what makes me good at my job.

"Always do," I reply with a loaded smile. I don't pretend with Ray: He knows me too well.

"I know, kid, I know," he says, offering a smile that mirrors my own.

My in-laws embrace me next, squeezing my hand and giving me a knowing look. For a lot of the people here, this night is a time for celebration and rejoicing: For us, it's remembrance.

My brother, James, walks in from the cold and empties his arms onto the living room floor. Coal and bread are among the items that spill onto mum's new carpet. I know she's going to have a shit fit when she notices and the thought of my perfect big brother getting into trouble makes me grin.

"Gifts from the first foot," he says, dramatically pulling his girlfriend, Helen, in for an extremely passionate (and inappropriate) kiss before encouraging everyone in the room to stand in a circle. Everyone joins hands and sing Auld Lang Syne, bouncing their arms in time with the music. No-one bothers asking me to join in anymore, they know what my answer will be.

James has always been the more outgoing one which, when you're an introvert like me, isn't such a terrible thing. He's a welcome distraction. People don't pay attention to me when he's around and he knows that's how I prefer things. Put me in a boardroom or have me pitch a campaign to a hundred people, no problem at all. Stick me in the middle of a family party and it's a different story.

It's not just our personalities that differ, other than our matching Hazel eyes, we don't look alike at all. He's tall, almost 6'5" and with shoulders built like a rugby player. I'm short and petite, barely 5'4" and, when we stand next to each other, I look even shorter.

As the music ends, Mum shushes everyone as she attempts to sneak into the front room with the worst kept secret that has ever graced our family. Every year, after the fireworks and singing have ended, she brings out my birthday cake like it's some shocking surprise. Every year, I dutifully blow out the candles and feign my excitement as my friends and family sing their terribly out of tune and out of time chorus of 'Happy Birthday'.

It's not happy though. I haven't had a happy birthday since I was twenty-one.

Aside from New Year's Eve, New Year's Day/My Birthday is my least favourite day of year but Mum always insists on having a party. This year, my 30th birthday, she went all out. Big cake, decorations, every single family member that still lives all crammed into her front room.

'Maggie Jones promise me that, if you aren't married by

thirty, you'll marry me.'

Although it's just a memory, his voice echoes in my ears, reminding me of the first time he proposed to me. We were just eight years old and it was the first time he kissed my cheek. The memory from twenty-two years ago was as vivid as yesterday.

As it happened, Philip didn't need to wait until we turned thirty. He proposed for real on my 18th birthday and we married the day after we graduated university. We were only twenty-one.

It was a small affair with only immediate family and friends in attendance but it was perfect, none the less. Philip was so handsome in his perfectly tailored, navy suit; he looked like he could be on the cover of GQ with his deep brown eyes and his usually shaggy, dark blonde hair styled neatly.

I felt like the luckiest girl alive that day. I *was* the luckiest girl alive.

For the first six months of our marriage, life was perfect. I had my husband (who I had loved since birth) and my dream job working with my dad and Ray. We had booked a trip of a lifetime to Iceland for our honeymoon so we could see the Northern Lights, something we had always dreamed of seeing. Our life together was just starting. We had dreams, plans of a family one day and the desire to grow old together.

We spent five days travelling around the Land of Fire and Ice. We had a spa day at the Blue Lagoon, walked across a glacier and visited the beautiful waterfalls and geysers. We had never seen such a beautiful landscape before and promised that we would be back again.

We had arrived back to London Heathrow on New Year's Eve, the night before my 22nd birthday. As we drove to Mum's house for her annual New Year's Eve party, we were in a car accident.

We hadn't been married long at all; I hadn't even had chance to legally change my name to his.

I survived with a few broken bones, a mild head injury and a collapsed lung but Philip... Well, he wasn't so lucky. They kept him alive long enough to donate his organs and, although my life fell apart that night (or rather when I woke up from my coma), so many other people were getting a second chance: Other families were seeing hope for the first time in forever. How could I resent that?

He was as selfless in death as he was in life.

My true hero.

My mum had held a joint New Year's Eve/Birthday party every year since my first birthday but continuing the parties was my mother-in-law's idea. She wanted the anniversary of her son's death to be a celebration of his life, to be a reminder that life is too short and the fact that I get to grow older each year is a blessing to each one of us.

How can I argue with her when she is so desperate to remember him like this?

As much as it was a painful reminder of what I had and what I have lost, I go because it's what they need. I go every year when I would rather be wallowing in my own grief. I smile, blow out my candles and thank my mum and dad for a lovely evening. I hug my mother and father-in-law, make sure they know how much I love them and then I return home to my small flat, alone, so I can try my best to remember him.

As a result of the head injury, I don't remember anything from that night but memories I've formed based on what people tell me feel real.

"Welcome to the thirties club. How are you holding up?" Laura asks as she brings me a large slice of cake, pulling me back to the present. Laura is Philip's twin sister and my best friend. She's gorgeous and tall with the longest legs and the brightest pink hair that sits neatly on her narrow shoulders. She's the only one who knows the real extent of my hatred for this party and, like me, she only endures it to appease her parents.

"You know, the usual. Cake's good though. I didn't think you could improve on last year's but you've done it," I say with my mouth full of the salted caramel, lighter-than-clouds sponge cake.

Laura is our resident cake maker. On every special occasion, Mum orders from Laura's bakery and for good reason: She's the best baker around. We keep telling her that she should enter *Bake Off: The Professionals* but she says she does it for love, not fame.

"I've already packed some up for you to take home, too. I assume you're leaving soon?"

"Yeah, I have a big meeting on the 2nd. I need to be well rested and focused."

"Okay, drinks are on Harry on Friday since he had to work tonight."

Harry is our other best friend. He lived in the student flats over the road from ours when he was a studying to be a paediatric nurse. The job suits him perfectly; he's strong and compassionate yet goofy and fun. He has a knack for making people smile and an ability to calm any situation, a godsend since Laura and I were both known for being slightly over dramatic.

"I'll be there. Promise"

At 1am, my taxi arrives and I say my goodbyes. I hold it together as we drive through residential London, Christmas lights flashing, music filling the air around me as the feeling gets heavier and heavier. It's not until I'm finally alone, wearing my new comfy pyjamas that Laura bought me for Christmas, that I finally let the tears flow free, like they do every year.

***

January 2nd is when my life goes back to normal, when I rebuild the walls that surround my vulnerability and lock up the sadness in a tiny box. Apparently, that's called compartmentalising my grief, so the hospital appointed therapist told me after the accident. I don't have time to dwell on the past for any longer than one day. I don't want to dwell on it, I can't change what happened but that doesn't mean my mind doesn't run through a thousand ways in which I could have done something differently.

On January 2nd, no matter what day of the week it is, I always go into the office to get a jump on the year ahead. This year, it's a Friday and most of the team have taken the day off so the office is still half empty when I arrive from my meeting, just before midday.

I was glad when the client called a meeting this morning as it gave me a reason to get up, wash my hair and put on my makeup when all I wanted to do was stay in bed.

"Good morning, Maggie. How was the meeting?" my assistant of 4 years, Sasha, asks as I place her favourite Maxwell's takeaway coffee down in front of her.

"Well, we've made progress. They've asked us to pitch an idea for their Easter campaign which starts just after Valentine's Day. I need you to call a meeting with senior staff for first thing Monday morning, please. We've only got six weeks to make this work and I need all hands-on deck."

"It'll have to wait, Maggs," a smooth, deep voice says from my doorway. I know who it is immediately. Only one person on the planet calls me 'Maggs'.

"Knock much?" I snap in annoyance at my familiar yet unwelcome visitor.

He rests his lean shoulder against my door frame in a way that would have most girls melting into a puddle on the floor. As he brushes his ink black hair away from his face, he brings his ice blue eyes up to meet mine, smiling his most perfectly charming smile my way. It may work on the floozies he usually keeps company with but he should know better than to try his charms on me. That's not to say I'm not occasionally dazzled by him - Okay, most of the time, he dazzles me but the only time it causes a reaction are the moments when he's not purposely trying to flirt with me or bait me, which are rare.

"What do you want, Jake?"

Jake Mills only ever comes to my office to point out a mistake in one of my business plans or annoy the living daylights out of me by telling me about his latest conquest. Right now, I don't have the time, nor the patience, to deal with his shit.

"We've been summoned."

I sigh in annoyance as he pushes away from the door frame to let me through. "Do you know why?"

"Nope," he answers as we make our way to the office belonging to our dads.

Jake is the only child of my dad's business partner and co-founder of Sixth Street Advertising, Raymond Mills. He is tall with a body that looks like it was chiselled from the finest marble and he is, of course, devastatingly handsome. He's also arrogant and obnoxious and a huge pain in my arse. I've known him since I was born. He is just over two years older than me, the same age as James. Growing up, he wasn't always entirely insufferable and, as kids, we got along well. Our parents are best friends, along with my in-laws, and we were all raised together; my brother, Philip,

Laura, Jake and me. We were a second generation of best friends.

It was childish and unrealistic, thinking that we would be friends forever, but something had changed between us when he left to study at Leeds University. I'm not sure if it was the distance between us or if it was intentional when he stopped talking to me out of the blue. I hoped he would have gotten over it when he started working as a Junior Graphic Designer in the Creative Department on the same day I started my internship as a Planning Assistant. I was so excited to have a friend here since everyone else was so daunting to my eighteen-year-old self.

A lot of people didn't have much faith in me: They thought I got an easy ride because I'm the boss' daughter, they thought that was the only reason I got my job. I assumed he would understand since he's the other boss' son and had worked just as hard as I had to get to where we were. I was wrong and, no matter how hard I tried, he just wasn't my friend anymore. I just couldn't put my finger on what it was that had changed but it didn't stop me trying to get him to talk to me, at first.

I gave up trying after the accident. I had bigger problems to think about than Jake's attitude towards me so I just got on with my job and chose to ignore him. I focused on perfecting my skills and worked my way up the company. At least I had started to gain some respect from my peers if not from him.

"Sorry, I couldn't make it the other night," he says, breaking the silence between us as we walk together through the unusually empty office. "James said you had a great night."

My brother would say that, he has my back completely and it sounds better than the truth that I couldn't wait to get home to wallow in my own self-pity. I should thank him for keeping my secret as last thing I want is for Jake to know how pathetic I am.

"Didn't know you were invited. You haven't stepped foot in my parents' house since my 18th birthday party when you got drunk and threw up in Mum's good vase."

"Come on, Maggie, it's not like I ruined your night. Philip is the one who got me drunk in the first place with those Jaeger bombs he was making. Your mum has forgiven me so surely you can too," he says, nudging me playfully while we walk. I've always been accident-prone so it's no surprise when I stumble over my own feet. Thankfully, he catches me before I crash right into an intern passing us in the corridor.

"I'm so sorry," I say to the young girl who can't seem to tear her eyes away from Jake when he winks at her. I roll my eyes as he hangs his arm casually around my shoulder. When we were kids, he would always do it to try and make Philip jealous. It would never work and everyone knew I only had eyes for the boy I loved. Besides, Jake was always a massive flirt with everyone he ever met and he didn't mean anything by it. It's just the way he was and, apparently, still is.

"She's really clumsy," he says as the girl bats her eyelashes at him.

"Ugh, come on, Prince Charming," I say, pushing him along but letting him keep his arm around me as the intern finds her voice.

"Goodbye, Mr Mills," she almost sings in a sickly-sweet voice.

Jake doesn't respond to her. Instead, he continues our walk with his arm firmly in its place while I make a dry heaving sound. When we walk like this, it takes me back to the way things were between us, back when we were friends. Maybe that's why I don't shake him off. Deep down, I miss him.

"Is someone jealous? You could just save us the trouble of all this backwards and forwards and just ask me out," he taunts me with a laugh.

"Pft, I'm not jealous. I'd just rather avoid a sexual harassment complaint against a senior member of staff."

"I'm glad you think of these things, Maggs."

"Well, someone has to," I say under my breath.

We've both come a long way since we started working here eleven years ago. We've both worked our way up and, now, I head up the strategic side of the business and Jake heads up the creative side. We often have to work together but we usually do this from separate floors of our building so he doesn't drive me completely batshit crazy.

"You don't need to worry; I don't dip my toe into the office pool, if you know what I mean," he says with a wink. "It's just a bit of harmless flirting."

I don't respond and, instead, I shrug out of his embrace as we approach Dad's office, an action to which he pouts at.

"Hi, Nikki, how are you?" I ask their assistant.

"You two look rather cosy," she whispers as we walk into the boardroom, leaving Jake talking in the hallway with his assistant, Thomas, who has appeared from nowhere.

"If 'cosy' means wanting to kick someone in the balls then yeah."

"Whatever. You could just screw him and get all this awkward sexual tension out of the way. He obviously fancies you and you can't tell me you don't find him sexy as hell." Nikki has never been one to mince her words.

I shoot her a look, warning her to shut up as he walks through the door to take his seat at the large boardroom table, Thomas dutifully following at his side.

Yeah, Jake is sexy as hell and maybe I do look when he casually leans back in his chair, resting his hands behind his head and showing off his sculpted biceps. He may be a huge shithead but there is no denying he is nice to look at. If he weren't such a knob, maybe I would fancy him but he's a massive knob, so I don't.

I don't join the others at the table right away. Instead, I stand with my back to them and look out of the large window to avoid getting caught by Nikki when I will inevitably check him out again.

I'm only human after all.

Out of the three board rooms we have in our office building, this one is my favourite. It has a killer view of the

Thames. Tower Bridge on the right, the Financial District across the river on the left, the Tower of London directly in front of us. It's the perfect location for office space. At Christmas, there's a lovely market down on the riverbank that sells food and gifts by independent traders. There's Potters Field Park, right next to City Hall, where you can sit in the sun and plenty of bars and restaurants within walking distance.

The view is beautiful all year round and today is no exception. The clouds are heavy as snowflakes begin to flurry towards the ground. Businessmen and women rush through the crowds of slow-moving tourists in a bid to get back to their offices on the first working day of the year before the snow really starts to fall.

There are people sat enjoying brunch under patio heaters and umbrellas in the restaurants' outdoor seating below, wearing big coats and covered by soft blankets, not letting the cold temperature ruin their plans.

"Your coffee," Sasha says, handing me my new mug. I smile when I see the photo of me, Philip, Laura and Harry that Harry got me as part of my Christmas present. It's a copy of a photobooth picture we took one night in Vodka Revolution in 2009. It's a terrible photo; we're all far too drunk but were having the best time!

I thank her and take the seat on Jake's other side, between him and Sasha, leaving the three seats opposite for Nikki, Dad and Ray.

"Sweetheart," Dad greets me, kissing my cheek as they walk in the room.

"Quite a party you missed, kid," Raymond says, "After you left, your brother got out the Sambuca and your mum set fire to the coffee table in the conservatory."

Jake doesn't say anything but raises his eyebrow at me. Clearly, James failed to mention to him that I left before the party really got going.

"Sounds about right. Mum loves a Flamin' Sambuca." Although my brother is almost thirty-three years old, he acts like a uni student on Freshers week and Mum thinks she can drink him under the table. She can't but she gives it a good go anyway. Luckily for James, his long-term girlfriend, Helen, is just as wild as he is.

"Well, thank you both for being here so promptly. We appreciate we didn't give you much notice," Dad says as he and Ray take their seats.

"We won't keep you too long. I understand you have a lot of work to start today, Maggie."

"I've got to start work on preparing the Stephenson's Chocolate pitch. I got the brief this morning. When everyone is back in the office next week, we can hit the ground running first thing Monday morning," I explain. "We'll be having a meeting to discuss so Sasha will forward you the minutes from this when we're done."

Dad and Ray agree before getting right down to business.

"Well, Kev," Raymond says, leaning back in his chair. His fingers wound together in front of his chest as his elbows sit on the arm rests. He looks almost nervous when he glances at my Dad. "Think I'll just cut to the chase. We would like to retire but, to do so, we need someone to take over the company."

I fail to find the words as Dad nods along in agreement. Mum has been on at him for years to retire, especially after his second heart attack and subsequent open-heart surgery a few years back, but he always brushes her off when she raises the issue of his health.

"Dad? Are you okay? Is it your heart?"

"No, sweetheart. I'm just old and tired."

"You're sixty!"

"Exactly. Things have changed since we started this firm. Times are different. It's time we let the next generation take the reins."

"So, what? You want one of us to take over?" Jake asks the question I didn't want to. Could I compete with Jake to get the position? I honestly don't know.

"Not exactly. We want you to work together. I couldn't have gotten this far without Ray's strategic planning," Dad answers him.

"And Kev has a creative eye that I simply do not have," Ray adds.

"You want us to run this company together?" I ask, unable to disguise the shock in my voice or hide it from my expression.

"Would that be so bad?" Jake says indignantly, turning in his seat to face me.

"Jake, if I say... I don't know... this notebook is black, you would argue that it's white," I say, holding up my own black notebook to drive home the point.

"Well, technically, the paper inside is white," he says smugly. I can feel my annoyance returning.

"You see?!" I exclaim, dropping my notebook to the table in front of me. "Insufferable."

"I'm not wrong," he argues back, holding my notebook open as proof. "The key to success is seeing things from an alternative perspective to your own. Give it a chance. You might grow to like it."

Highly unlikely!

"Work together on the Stephenson's pitch. You'll see how important you are to each other's successes," Dad says, interrupting our argument.

"Are you serious?" I don't have time to process what they're saying before Dad abruptly ends the conversation.

"We've made our choice. It's either pass the company to the both of you or find a buyer. Work together or not at all. Before you argue, your new *joint* office will be ready to move into on Monday."

"Then we'll do our best," Jake says, smiling. "Right, Maggs?"

"Of course," I say, putting on my best poker face. On the

outside, I'm portraying calm and confident but, on the inside, I'm pushing down the fury I feel when I think about having to share this account with Jake, let alone having to run the company *and* share an office space with him.

CHAPTER TWO

I'm the first person to leave the boardroom to dash back to my office, leaving Jake behind to make small talk with our dads. Sasha follows, hot on my heels, sensing my impending outburst.

"Can you believe this? They want me to work with him. Like partners," I say as I pace the floor in front of my desk in annoyance.

"Well... Yeah, I can," Sasha says, being the voice of reason that I need but don't want to listen to right now. "You've both as much right as each other to take over the company. You're both more than capable of doing it."

"But, Sasha, we've worked so hard on this and now we just have to hand over half the credit. Not to mention we have to share an office!" I say, throwing my hands in the air for emphasis.

"I, for one, am really excited about this," Sasha says sincerely.

I huff out a breath of annoyance. I knew she would be excited about this. The way she and Thomas stare dreamily at one another whenever they are in the same room is actually quite cute. I'm not sure if anything ever did happen between them after the

Christmas party two years ago and I never asked her as I try not to get involved but it's hard to avoid the idle office gossip.

"Maggie, you're overreacting and you know it. Jake would have gotten involved in this project eventually. Besides, what I wouldn't give to share an office with that delicious man. Many women would kill to be you," she says with a dreamy smile.

"I know you're joking but that is exactly why I don't want to share an office with him. He just needs to glance at a girl and their knickers spontaneously combust! You should have seen him with an intern earlier. Ugh. It's going to be hell. He's just so arrogant and egotistical and-"

"Devilishly handsome?" he finishes for me as my head snaps around at the sound of his voice. "Are you that worried that your knickers are going to spontaneously combust?"

"Oh my god, learn how to bloody knock!" I yell, startled and embarrassed. I can feel the heat of the blush spread up my neck and settle in my cheeks.

"What happened to your 'open door policy'?" he quotes me, grinning while he leans against my door frame and crosses his ankles, an action that has suddenly become a habit of his. He straightens up when he sees the look I shoot at him.

"I was going to call you a shithead, if you really wanted to know."

"Come on, Maggs. We can put our differences aside and get on with it. Can you remember when we were kids? We'd talk about the day we would eventually take over. You couldn't wait and were so pissed off that I was going off to uni and you had to wait another two years. I know we lost each other somewhere along the way but this is the best thing for *our* company and, you never know, we could become friends again."

I stop in my tracks, the weight of his words settling in my chest as I turn to face him again. I can see by the way he is looking at me that he meant what he said.

I hate that he's right. I've dreamed of this day for as long as I can remember and I haven't reacted very well to the news at all. More than that, I hate that this man (once one of my closest friends) is virtually a stranger to me. How did we get so lost?

When he uses the nickname he gave me when I was a teenager in his rough yet silky-smooth voice, it takes me right back to that time. I hated that nickname when I was younger which is why no-one else calls me 'Maggs'. When he says it, I don't hate it at all. For so long I wanted to hear him say my name because that would mean we were speaking again.

"I know, you're right," I admit. " I have rules if this is going to work. I don't want to see, hear or read about any of your sexual conquests. I want you to take this seriously; that means be here on time and give it everything you've got."

"Maggie Jones, I'll give you every last inch of me," he says with a roguish smirk, slightly changing my words to make it sound much dirtier than it needs to be. "Okay, I'll stop with the unnecessary flirting but I also have requests... You need to be less - I don't know - stressy. Try be more laid back, less bossy, more open to seeing my point of view."

"I can do that," I say which makes Sasha bark out a laugh, earning herself a glare from me. "I can!" I insist.

"One last thing. Once a week, on a day of your choosing, you'll have dinner with me. Just me, no inviting buffers like James or Laura or Helen. Just You and me," he adds, grinning.

He cannot be serious. I can barely stand to be around him at work, never mind outside of the office in the real world.

"What? Why?"

"It doesn't have to be dinner, it can be anything you want to do. Maybe if you see me outside of these walls, you might actually see that I'm not as big of a shithead as you think I am." A smile slips onto my lips when he uses my favourite insult.

I glance at Sasha for support but she doesn't notice, she's too busy staring at the floor and trying to hide her own smile, although it's clear she's trying not to laugh uncontrollably.

I don't say anything so Jake breaks the silence again. "I can't wait to tell you about all my 'sexual conquests'," he says, echoing me with air quotes.

"Okay, we can do dinner," I say in mild annoyance.

Truth is, I want to believe that we can be friends again but I can't just ignore everything that's happened between us. He was willing to throw our friendship away in the first place, who's to say he won't do it again.

"So, how about tonight?"

"Not tonight, I'm going to The George with Laura and

Harry."

"Saturday?"

"Sure, that works."

"Right, well, now I know you two aren't going to rip each other's heads off, I'm going to go and organise this meeting and leave you two to you chat some more." Sasha winks before leaving me to deal with Jake on my own.

I unpack my laptop and turn it on while Jake walks around my office, picking books off their shelves and leafing through the business magazines he's found on the small coffee table nestled in the corner. He sits down on the high back chair and strokes the arms, admiring the feel of the navy velvet. I glance over at him and it looks like he is taking in the room, like it's the first time he's really took notice.

"So, why did you leave your own birthday party early? You were always the life of that party growing up. You didn't want to stick around for the pyrotechnics?" he says, breaking the silence. I was hoping he had forgotten about that little bit of information, since the reason for me leaving is not something I'd like to go into detail with him.

At one time, I would have been the last one to go to sleep on New Year's Day. Now, I leave before the party gets to the exciting part like when Mum and James try to out-do each other on Jaeger Bombs and Flamin' Sambuca Shots.

Instead of coming up with a lie to explain why I left, I ignore the question completely. "Do you want me to run through this pitch with you before we bring in the teams? It will take a while. I've been working on it for a long time."

He smiles, acknowledging the fact I've avoided his question but doesn't push further. Instead, he pulls around a chair and sits beside me.

"Yeah, show me."

***

Later that night, I meet Harry and Laura in The George, as planned. The George is a typical 'old man' pub that has been recently taken over by the previous owner's grandson. It still has the original vibe of a traditional English pub but with added modern touches like 2 for 1 cocktails, themed quiz nights and a band that plays on a Saturday night. The old beer garden that leads off the main road has been transformed with an ivy and fairy light covered pergola. The path is adorned with beautiful red, orange and green Acer trees, hiding it from the road so it feels private and secretive.

The best thing about this pub is that we can all walk home which is the main reason we drink here most Friday nights.

"You have to share an office with Jake Mills!? God, I haven't seen him for years. Follow him on Insta though. How *will* you get any work done?" Laura says, grinning at me as she pulls his profile up to show Harry.

"Not everyone is as perverted as you are, Laura.

Especially not our Maggie," Harry says with a wink as he places our drinks down in front of us. He takes his seat next to Laura and rests his long arms on the back of the booth we sit in. "Although, I see what you mean. Has he always this hot or has he had a glow up?" he adds, raising his eyebrows and scrolling down the page.

"Shit, Harry, you've liked his picture from a year ago," Laura says as she quickly unlikes it. "He's going to know I was stalking him now. And yes, he was always that fit. I always thought he had a thing for Maggie, too, but then he went weird on us."

"Maybe he can be the one to re-pop her cherry," Harry says, grinning over his glass.

"Harry, that's disgusting!" I protest.

"But, also, a fantastic Idea?" Laura adds.

From the moment we met Harry at our local student nightclub, krumping on a podium to Beyonce's *'Crazy in Love'*, I knew we would be best friends. I'll always remember when he dragged an overly confident Philip up to dance with him and that was it; Harry was a part of our family. It was long after Jake abandoned us and I think it was a welcome relief for Philip to have a male in the group again.

"That's not the only thing. I'm having dinner with him tomorrow night," I confess.

As soon as the words leave my mouth I regret not waiting until they had finished drinking their drinks and I narrowly miss getting soaked by the wine they both spit out over the table.

"You're going on a date with Jake Mills!?" Laura squeals with excitement, attracting the attention of several tables around us.

"Keep your voice down," I stage shout. "And no, not a date. He wants me to trust him and he thinks it'll help if I get to know him better. If we become friends again."

"You've known him your whole life. Surely, you know him by now. Are you sure it's not a date?"

"He was rather persistent about it but it doesn't mean anything. I'll go to dinner and get to know him again and then we can find a way to coexist peacefully. Can we change the subject now, please?"

Laura thinks about it for a moment before shrugging.

"Well, we'll see. Anyway, moving on from your work-based drama, let's get down to business," Laura says, pulling out her note pad. "Harry, I need to know your resolutions."

Harry pulls his note pad up on his phone and clears his throat confidently. "I am going to lose a stone and find the love of my life"

"So, same as last year then?" Laura confirms, writing it down.

"Yep, what about you?"

"I am going to learn a new hobby. I'm open to suggestions, if you have any? Nothing dangerous or too expensive. And I'm going to start going to the gym I joined last January and have yet to do my induction at," she says, writing it in her notebook before closing it with a satisfied smile.

Every year, she does this and, every year, I have nothing to add so she's surprised when I speak.

"I'm going to start dating again, that's my resolution. I think it's about time I get myself back out there. Say 'yes' to doing more and trying new things. Return to the land of the living."

My friends look at me blankly, stunned by my declaration. Since Philip died, I haven't expressed any interest in meeting anyone new so I think they had resigned to the fact I would be alone for the rest of my life. As much as my parents (and Philip's parents, too, for that matter) have tried to set me up with their friends' sons, I've always found a way to avoid it but something has changed recently. Maybe turning thirty triggered something in my brain because I was suddenly very aware that I had barely lived my twenties at all.

When was the last time I did anything other than work? I can't remember.

Laura shakes her head as if she's not hearing right. "You want to meet someone?"

"I don't know if I want to settle down right away or have a bunch of babies but I'm thirty! My biological clock is ticking so maybe going on a date is a good start."

"Give me your phone. I'm setting you up on some apps. Tinder, E-Harmony, just the basics to get you started," Laura says as she and Harry ignore me, tapping ferociously on my iPhone. I have anxiety just thinking about what they're doing. "Plenty of

Fish?" she asks as Harry nods to her in agreement before concentrating on the tiny screen again.

"Does James know you're here tonight?" Harry asks.

"Oh, hey, there's your brother," Laura says at the same time. She waves across the bar to him. "Oh, God, Jake is with him and that guy. What's his name?"

"Simon? Oh, he is to die for. I have not stopped dreaming about him since your brother's birthday party last year," Harry says, fussing his longer-than-usual brown hair and straightening his slim fit, checked shirt. "How do I look? Please let them sit with us, Maggie. That guy is hot and gay. You know the only guys I seem to be attracted to are straight, except this one. Please, please, please."

Before I can protest, my brother waves back and makes his way over to our table, followed by Jake and a nervous looking Simon. I don't know him all too well but he seems nice enough.

"Mind if we join you?" James asks, nudging Simon over to the empty spot next to Harry. I smile as I see what is going on. Simon is just as taken by Harry as Harry is by Simon.

"Sure," I say as I scooch along to make room in the six-seater booth for my brother when Jake slides in, flinging his arm to rest on the seat behind me. Great, my new-slash-old bestie.

"Hi, Maggs," he says, flashing me a wide smile. "Fancy seeing you here."

I give him a look that says, '*Yeah, funny, since I told you that this was exactly where I was going to be*'.

My brother takes our drink order and heads to the bar, whisking Laura away to help him.

"Sorry for just turning up. Simon really likes Harry and you said he would be here. What kind of wingman would I be if I didn't help him hook up, right?" Jake whispers, leaning in close to my ear so Simon and Harry can't hear. I can feel his breath as he speaks and it sends prickles down my neck.

"You don't need to explain anything to me. Harry will thank you for playing cupid." I smile. I look over at the two new love birds cooing over each other already. Man, they work fast.

"Can you tolerate me for a little while, then?" His voice is lower than usual and I look at his arm still around me but he makes no attempt to move it. I get the feeling he's flirting with me again. Usually, I can read him like a book but, for the first time, I can't.

"I suppose I can try," I quip back at him.

He grins at me, his eyes sparkling in the warm lighting of the pub. "Be careful. You might even start to like me."

"I never said I don't like you, Jake," I say, returning his grin with a small, flirtatious smile. "I just think you're a bit of a shithead."

"That's good to know." He laughs, raking his fingers through his hair, his cheeks slightly pinker than normal as James places our fresh drinks in front of us, oblivious to our exchange.

Jake passes me my drink from the end of the table, his gaze lingering on me before he holds his own glass up to mine in a cheers.

***

A few hours pass and Helen and her friend, Cylvie, finally arrive. Helen and James met when he was doing a construction job at the Victoria Apollo. She was in the Wicked ensemble at the time and had not long graduated from the London Academy of Music and Dramatic Arts. I couldn't think of a better match for my brother.

Helen and I have always gotten on well. Cylvie, on the other hand… Not so much. She's tall, skinny and so perfectly French but she has the personality of a wet paper bag. No matter how much I try get her to warm to me by asking questions, complementing her or including her in conversations, she just looks at me as if I'm speaking Swahili or something. I know her English is flawless so it's not like she can't understand me.

Even Laura, who is a *sees-the-best-in-everyone* kind of person, can't stand her.

Despite Cylvie being her usual bitchy self, I have enjoyed the extra company tonight. What has surprised me most is that having Jake here has also been rather nice. He's good company when he's not trying to torment me and he's quite funny when he isn't pushing me towards breaking point. Maybe it's the alcohol he keeps buying me that is making me warm up to him more.

I noticed a change in him this afternoon when we had a joint meeting with our Heads of Department in preparation for working together over the coming weeks. He let me take the lead and only spoke up when I invited him to. It took me off guard to see him take a step back when he is used to being the big man in charge.

As expected, Harry and Simon have gone off to their own booth and are busy trying to taste each other's tonsils. For someone so shy, Simon really came into his own after a few drinks. He and Harry looked so comfortable together, it was like they'd known each other for a lifetime. Maybe this is the year Harry gets to tick off one of his resolutions.

"So, you not on the pull tonight, mate?" James asks Jake, nodding towards Cylvie who is draped seductively over the pool table as she and Helen play.

"Nope, got a deal with my partner here," he says, draping his arm around my shoulder and, once again, I enjoy the feel of his touch. I roll my eyes at him as I try to ignore that fact and he responds with a small chuckle. "What was your rule again? Something about not seeing or hearing about my 'sexual conquests'?"

"At work, yeah. I'm not going to stop you chatting someone up in a pub. Feel free. It's not like Cylvie hasn't made it blatantly obvious she's desperate to shag you," I say, unable to keep the edge out of my voice when I say her name.

"There's that jealousy again," he says, teasing me. "Think I'm good here anyway," he adds with a shrug.

It was as if she knows we're talking about her as she comes and sits opposite Jake, not even trying to look at me or James.

"What's that, Laura? My round? Okay," my brother shouts to Laura at the bar who hasn't said a word but looks at us in confusion before he makes his escape. As much as he doesn't dislike Cylvie, it's obvious he can't stand to be around her as much as the rest of us.

Jake grips me tighter, moving his hand to fall around my waist and pulling me closer into his side. "Protect me," he whispers to me, almost hiding in my hair. I give a little giggle as though he's said something flirty for effect and take hold of his other hand that sits in his lap.

"You two?" Cylvie spits, looking almost nauseous.

"What can I say? She called me a shithead and I melted," Jake says, nuzzling my hair again.

"We're just, you know, friends," I say, truthfully, although I look at him as though we're sickeningly in love. I clearly missed my calling as an actress. Jake cocks his eyebrow at me in amusement.

"Call me when you see sense and want an upgrade, Mills," she says, looking me up and down with another loathsome look before getting up out of the booth and heading straight for the door.

"Where did Cylvie go?" Helen asks, looking around when she gets back to the table a moment later.

"Excuse me," I say as I push Jake away from me so I can climb out of the booth over him, not waiting for him to move out of my way.

"Maggs! Maggie!" Jake shouts after me but I don't listen to him as I make a beeline for the ladies' toilets.

It's funny how another woman can cut you down so easily with one simple look, a look that says more words than she could ever say out loud.

I wash my hands and splash the icy water up my arms. As I dry my hands, I look at myself in the floor to ceiling mirror and it's as though all my imperfections are glowing for the entire world to see, flashing neon lights drawing attention to every lump and bump. I'm not stick thin like Cylvie; I'm not supermodel gorgeous like Helen or even quirky and confident like Laura.

I have cellulite and little, silver stretch marks and that doesn't bother me because I have nice parts too. I have long, blonde hair that's highlighted regularly and my skin is almost flawless besides a monthly, hormonal breakout. I try to do yoga every now and then and I eat right most of the time but I also enjoy myself. Cider and carbs aren't ideal but they're tasty and that's all that matters, right? I enjoy myself and I'm happy in my own, perfectly average skin.

When Cylvie looked at me and took note of every part of me that is inferior to her, it struck me.

I'm no Michelle Keegan but I'm not ugly either. Is it ridiculous to think that a man like Jake could fancy a girl like me? Not that I want him to fancy me but is it that unbelievable?

"Get your shit together," I say to myself in the mirror before I realise there is someone standing in the doorway watching me.

"She's a bitch and we all know it. Don't listen to her," Laura says, linking her arm through mine. "You're worth a million Cylvies and she knows it. She's just jealous because Jake showed you more attention tonight than he could show her in a lifetime."

I don't respond, I just look at her, my beautiful best friend who always knows what to say.

"Come on, the witch left, anyway. Let's get another drink," she says, our arms still linked as we head back into to the pub.

"What are you doing tomorrow?" James asks as I take a seat opposite him and away from Jake. He frowns making a little crease appear between his eyebrows. "Mum wants to come into the city. She wants to go to Harrods. Since Auntie Sarah is coming from New York to visit, she wants to buy some ridiculously overpriced biscuits or meats or some shit, I don't know. I thought we could meet her for lunch somewhere nice, maybe an afternoon tea in their tearoom. She'd love that."

Auntie Sarah is Dad's sister and she is always trying to one up Mum. She lives in Manhattan and shops on Fifth Avenue so thinks she's way above us all.

"Sorry, I'm working."

"You're working? Tomorrow? It's Saturday. Your dad is your boss. Surely, that means you can slack off a bit."

"I'm the boss' daughter. It means I have to work twice as hard for half the respect," I say, as a matter of fact. Sad but true.

"People respect you. You just have to look at your team to see they worship the ground you walk on," Jake says, butting into our conversation, leaving Laura and Helen to their own conversation.

"And what about you? It feels like I'm treading water with you sometimes," I ask, raising my eyebrows. He seems taken aback with my sudden change in my attitude towards him and doesn't say anything to dispute what I said which, to me, speaks volumes.

"What about tomorrow, late afternoon? After she's finished shopping? Grab an early dinner?" James asks.

"Yeah, I suppose that would work"

"Woah, woah, woah," Jake says, waving his hands at me. "You forgot our plans already?"

"You two have plans? Together? Tomorrow night?" my brother, asks looking between us. "Saturday night?"

"Yeah, I got us a table at the Paternoster Chop House."

"You booked us a table at the *'First Dates'* restaurant!?" I ask, stunned.

"Sasha said you've always wanted to go and that you love the show so I called a friend who knows someone who got us a last-minute reservation."

"Hang on, back up a moment. You two are going on a date? To the *'First Dates'* restaurant, no less, and you didn't tell me?" my brother asks, looking between us with the biggest smile on his face. He almost looks pleased that his best friend with a big reputation for shagging anything with a pulse is going out for dinner with his little sister.

"It's not a date, it's one of his stupid rules for working together."

"It's not stupid, it's so you can see I'm not a complete knob," he says as though it explains things.

"But you are a complete knob," James says with a laugh.

"Not all the time, just *some* of the time," he quips back.

"If you insist on going to work, finish early and you can meet me and Mum for lunch at Harrods. Half past twelve, no excuses. You've got some making up to do after you left early the other night. You know she worries about you, more so this time of year. Just show her you're okay."

I know I'm not going to win the argument. My brother is right, I should really make the effort, I said so myself when I declared my New Year's resolutions to Laura and Harry.

As much as I hate shopping, especially in Harrods on a Saturday lunchtime and *especially* when the January sales are on, Mum loves it and I love Mum so I agree.

CHAPTER THREE

When I walk into my office on Saturday morning, the last thing my hungover self expected to find lounging in *my* chair with his feet on *my* desk was Jake Mills.

"You, Ms Jones, are late," he says, dramatically looking at his empty wrist as though he's looking at the time.

"You are way too enthusiastic for 9 am on a Saturday and what do you mean I'm 'late'? It's 4 minutes past 9," I say, taking the Maxwell's takeaway cup he hands me and smelling the mocha inside. "How do you know my coffee order?"

"I sent a text to Thomas last night, got him to ask Sasha what time you usually arrive on a Saturday. She said 9 am so I arrived at 8:55. You always have a takeaway cup from Maxwell's so I went there first and asked them your order and this is what they gave me. You know, you could just say 'thank you'."

"Thank you," I quickly add. "Sorry. I'm not usually so rude when people surprise me with a coffee. My brain is a little foggy this morning."

"That's why I bought these," he says, throwing boxes of Paracetamol and Ibuprofen to me which I completely miss and have to scoop up from the floor. "I wasn't sure which one you prefer so I bought both to be safe. It was an impressive volume of alcohol you consumed last night. I have to say, you drank way more than I thought you could."

"It's my hidden talent," I reply in a deadpan tone, shrugging my jacket off and removing my dark RayBans that kept the winter sun from blinding me on my way here. "So, why did you come here? Why didn't you just come to my flat? What if I'd stayed home, hungover?"

"I thought it would be more of a dramatic gesture to surprise you here. I knew you'd be here because, every time I told you to take the day off, you looked at me like I had grown an extra head or something," he says, smiling. "You're meeting your mum and brother at 12:30 and I thought you might like some help to make sure you're not late. Plus, it's a good excuse to find out what you do all day. I've never really thought much about it but I'd really like to know."

I look at him in complete bewilderment. His sudden personality transplant and the bulldozer that has taken up residence in my brain overnight aren't helping me process anything right now.

"You're serious, aren't you, about this working together stuff?"

"I am, Maggs. I know I don't show it to you often, if at all, but I really am committed to this company. I love my job; how many people can say that and mean it? I want to show you how committed I am to you, too, as your business partner. I know I've not given you much reason to trust that but I hope I can prove it to you now."

A smile spreads over my face as I listen to his passionate speech: His words are genuine. I feel like I'm seeing him for the first time in years. He's being honest and almost vulnerable when he asks me to trust him and, with every word, I find myself softening towards him.

"Okay, let's get started," I say, shooing him out of my chair, still smiling like the Cheshire Cat.

I set my laptop up, pull out the files I'm working on and he patiently sits on the other side of my desk, carefully watching my every move.

"What?" I say, putting my coffee down, unable to take his staring much longer.

"I had fun last night. It felt great to be hanging out with you and Laura again. Harry is hilarious too, you know. When Simon let him up for air, he seemed like a really cool bloke."

"They seemed to really click and Harry is the best."

"You warmed up to me, too, I could tell. I feel like I got to take a peek behind those big, brick walls you've built. It was nice."

"That's what alcohol does to a person. Releases those inhibitions, right? Gets people to let down their guard?"

"Do you want to talk about what it was that Cylvie said that made you shut down again?"

I drum my fingers on my desk, the anxious energy I am

trying to control making an attempt to escape. I scrunch my fingers to stop the tapping, hating myself for letting her get to me the way she did. The look and the thousand mean words she implied with it rattle around in my brain almost uncontrollably.

I remember what my therapist said about compartmentalising, about how I shouldn't do it and that it's not healthy in the long run because what happens when there is no more space in my brain to lock those thoughts away? I remember what she said and I ignore it, as I usually do. I stuff those words away and lock the box up tight. It's tough to shut that part of my brain down and return to my work but it's what I do. It's what I've done for a long time when faced with something I'm not prepared to think about.

"So, this pile here," I say, pointing to a pile of files on my desk, "These are the accounts that are waiting for my approval for the week. Deadline for this to reach me is 4 pm Friday. I go through this pile so they are ready to either be reworked or go down to you to be distributed first thing Monday morning and – Well, you know what happens after that."

"You do this every Saturday?" Jake says, looking stunned and not addressing the fact I changed the subject.

"Yeah," I say with a shrug.

"So, because I'm an arsehole and demand these first thing Monday morning, you have to work all weekend?"

"I wouldn't have put it quite as eloquently but... Yeah."

"Screw that. I'm sorry. I didn't know you had to work

today to get this done. Like I said, I haven't put much thought into what you do really or how long it takes to get it right. We'll change the system; we can come up with something else together. You shouldn't have to do this every week."

He seems genuinely shocked that I'm here to get the work ready for him but how else did he think I got it done ready for Monday?

"I wish it were as simple as not doing it, Jake, but I have certain responsibilities. I have jobs that need to be done and they should be done perfectly, otherwise what's the point in doing them at all? If that means working on a Saturday, I'll do it. I have nothing better to do besides sitting alone in my empty flat."

"Hey, Maggs," he says as he reaches over to stop my fingers drumming on the desk again. I didn't even realise I was doing it this time. "We'll figure it all out. With the extra time you have on a weekend because of that, we can fill it with whatever you want to do. You know, as part of our deal."

I look down at my hand enveloped in his and he squeezes it reassuringly before pulling back.

"This pile here are the plans that have been reworked," I say, pointing to a smaller pile of just four files. "That won't take long for me to sign off as I've already gone through them once. They'll be perfect now."

"Perfect, huh?"

"Perfect," I agree, straightening the pile.

"What's this?" he asks picking up the large lever arch file

sat at the end of my desk.

"That's for Stephenson's. It needs to be archived," I reply. Jake looks at me blankly so I continue. "It's the research. A few weeks back, when we got the chance to pitch for the job, we conducted market research on their various products. That's a sample of 500 people. We held 50 focus groups of 10 people and collated the data to present to them. It's what ultimately won us the opportunity to work on their Easter campaign. No one else had done that for them."

"And you do this for every account?"

"Yeah. It's not always to that scale and it's a team effort, not just me. In my opinion, it's the most important part of the complete process. You could have a fantastic campaign but none of that matters if you don't know your audience. It's all well and good to have a message but we need to know how to communicate it, we need to know how the audience wants to receive the message and when they want to receive it. If you don't know that, you don't get the optimum reach, you know?"

He smiles like he is seeing me for the first time in years. He underestimated me, just like the rest of the company.

"This is a lot of information," he says, flicking through the pages. "It's impressive, Maggs."

"Yeah, we sift through this and find what the common factors are and condense it for the brief you see."

"Everything here is so organised," he says as he wanders around my office again. "It's no surprise you're the best we have."

"Thanks," I say, slightly flushed at his compliment.

We continue working our way through the pile of folders for the rest of the morning. He asks questions and inputs where he can and, before we know it, we're caught up with plenty of time for me to make the journey to Knightsbridge.

"Jake?" I ask as we step out of our office onto the busy riverside walkway. "Next week, would you mind if I spend a day with you, down in Creative?"

"I would love that," he says with a smile I've not seen on him for a long time. It's not the smile he reserves for charming endless amounts of women or the hearty grin he has when he's being mischievous with my brother. This smile is soft and his eyes are shining. I would say this smile is his most genuine and it's making me feel (for lack of a better description) weak at the knees.

***

"So, how are you, sweetheart?" Mum asks as I kiss her on the cheek and take my seat at the table - On time, might I add, thanks to Jake.

It's been years since I've eaten in the luxurious Harrods Tea Room. Each place is set to perfection with the finest china and silverware, a view of the beautiful blossom tree from each seat. Sunlight streams through the sky light, filling the room with sun rays that bounce from the Georgian pillars to the gold, Art Deco carpet. It's the epitome of class and luxury.

"I'm good, Mum. You look lovely."

Annie Jones has never looked her age; she's tall and slender with cropped, ginger hair and a fringe that frames her beautiful face. Only the slightest signs of aging show in her shallow wrinkles and laughter lines which she says she owes this to her lifetime supply of '*Oil of Olay*'. Mum was a teacher at our local primary school. Luckily, I was never in her class and I can't imagine what it would have been like to have your Mum as your teacher. She had a reputation for being kind and patient with all her students. The kids loved her, the mums respected her and the dads fancied her.

"I'm surprised you made it. I figured you'd either be home and hungover or at the office and hungover," James comments.

"Me, hungover? At Harrods? No way," I say, feigning indignation with a smile. "Besides, Jake actually helped me get things finished so I would be on time."

"Jake? Jake was at work on a Saturday?"

"Yeah, I was just as surprised as you are," I say as mum orders Afternoon Tea for three and the waiter pours our tea and accompanying champagne.

I suppose it's not often mum has both children to herself and so she wants it to be special.

I stifle a laugh as my brother picks up his delicate teacup in his extra-large hands. With his friends, he's this funny, annoying, lad's lad. With Helen, he's the best thing since sliced bread. Here, with mum, he's just her little boy.

The waiter quickly returns with a vast selection of finger sandwiches, fruit and cheese scones and mini cakes. I have no idea where to start but my stomach rumbles loudly, telling me it needs food.

"So, how is Jacob these days? It's been a while since I've seen him," Mum says. "He doesn't tell his mother much and I know she worries about him."

"He's fine. It was better than I thought, working with him this morning. He wasn't as frustrating as he normally is."

"And he's taking her on a date to the *'First Dates'* restaurant tonight," James says to Mum with a grin, knowing he's thrown me under the bus.

"It's not a date," I quickly retort as mum's eyes light up at the possibility of me dating. "I think he's trying to prove to me that he will be a good business partner."

"Jacob has always been a lovely man. You could do a lot worse," Mum argues.

"He's a lovely man with a reputation," I counter.

"Well, sometimes reputations aren't all they seem," James says as he shoves a full finger sandwich in his mouth.

I stick out my tongue while Mum scolds him for his lack of table manners. No matter how old, I am I will always relish in my perfect big brother being told off, it's what little sisters are made for.

"We'll see how long it lasts before he turns back into the giant pain in my ar-"

"Language." Now it's James' turn to stick out his tongue.

"Sorry, Mum."

"Jake is my best mate. He has a lot to give and, when he says he wants something, he won't quit, believe me. If he's told you he wants to be a good business partner, you should believe him."

"Yeah, he was my best friend too, remember? That meant nothing to him."

"I'm not saying what he did wasn't wrong but, if you knew half the story, maybe you'd see things his way too."

"Do you have anything to wear tonight? It's a posh restaurant. Maybe I could get you a new dress?" Mum says, interrupting us before we start to bicker. "We can always go to Harvey Nicks next, if you can't find anything here. Or maybe even Selfridges?"

She smiles at me so excitedly that I'm hit with a pang of guilt.

Before the accident, Mum and I were inseparable. We would go out shopping and to lunch all the time. We would go on girls' weekends away or on a night out at the theatre together. We would sometimes go alone, sometimes with Laura, her mum, Angela, and Jake's mum, Margaret.

My favourite thing to do with Mum was visit a Christmas Market. We travelled to a different place each year, sometimes as close as Winter Wonderland in Hyde Park or further away to places like Edinburgh or Manchester. My favourite trip was our last one when we travelled to Belgium, the December before the accident. We spent hours walking around the cold market town of Bruges with frites and gluhwein getting us in the festive mood, not to mention the delicious waffles and chocolates we overindulged on.

After the accident, I couldn't face doing anything anymore, not just with Mum but with anyone. I couldn't even look Phillip's parents in the eye. All I wanted to do was go to work and hide away in my flat watching crappy TV. I felt that I had a responsibility to keep everyone together. After all, I'm the one that made it out of that accident alive. I owe my life to someone so may as well spend it protecting the people I love.

I wasn't always so guarded or put together. Some days, I couldn't hide how distraught I was or how much I struggled with my physiotherapy. It upset Mum to see me in so much pain and I hated the fact that she worried about me so much. So, I acted like it didn't hurt anymore and it was easier to pretend when she couldn't see me.

After a few years, she eventually she stopped asking me to do things with her. I knew it hurt her every time I refused her invitations so, at first, I was glad when she had stopped asking. Now, I miss those times more than anything.

"Thanks, Mum, I'd really like that," I say as she squeezes my hand.

James smiles at me, too, knowing how happy I've made her with a small act of shopping.

"I'll come with you two, I need to pick up something for Helen's birthday and have no idea where to start with women things."

I make a promise to myself that I'll make more of an effort with Mum, to take her places and make more plans with her. Maybe we could even go away for a weekend. I know she'd love it. I owe her that much after the support she's given me my whole life.

***

This is not a date. This is not a date. This is. Not. A. Date.

Why do I feel so bloody nervous?!

It's Jake. We're friends again.

It's not like I hadn't spent the morning with him and that was fine. It was more than fine. It was easy and comfortable. I blame James for getting in my head this afternoon. He knows more than he lets on about what happened with Jake. I should ask him about it but I'm scared that I'll not like the answer.

I walk up the steps at St Paul's tube station 15 minutes before I'm meant to so I don't expect to see Jake waiting for me, looking like he's just stepped off the catwalk at New York Fashion Week in his dark grey, wool coat and his perfectly fitted, black dress trousers.

But there he stands.

His inky hair is gorgeously dishevelled and pushed back

from his face, his smile so wide it makes his eyes light up. In the office, his attire consists of jeans, black vans that look like they've seen better days and a T-shirt with some sort of graphic on the front. Not that I pay close attention to what he wears nor do I care about what he wears in the office but, to see him here, dressed in dress shoes paired with a slim fit, black shirt, is pleasantly surprising.

"Like what you see?" he says, mocking my obviously dazed expression as my eyes drink him in. He looks gorgeous.

"You look good, Jake. Who knew?" I joke.

"Thanks. I think," he says, leading the way to the restaurant. "So, my mum called me this afternoon. Apparently, your mum called her and told her I was taking you out on a 'posh date'. She told me not to be an 'arsehole' to you. Those exact words came from her mouth," he says, laughing and using air quotes. I'm thankful it's dark when I feel my cheeks heat and I groan inwardly with embarrassment.

"I've told her a thousand times that it's not a date. She doesn't listen. You could hang up on your mum, though. I was shopping with mine and trying on ridiculously expensive dresses." It was so much fun.

He laughs in agreement as we approach the familiar glass doors, just like on the TV.

"Now, I know this isn't a date and you know this isn't a date but please don't fight me on the bill. I know you've got the whole strong, independent woman thing going on, which I love and respect that about you, but just let me have this, please? We're also getting fillet steaks with all the trimmings because the reviews say it's incredible."

I go to argue but he presses his finger on my lips before the words come out.

"That's very kind, thank you," I mumble, his finger still pressing against my lips. "But, just know, I'm paying for the next one."

"I suppose that's fair," he says, opening the door for me like a gentleman. He takes my coat and passes it to the hostess before abruptly stopping. "Wow!" he adds as his eyes travel slowly down the length of my body.

"What?" I say as I straighten out the black, figure hugging dress that stops mid-thigh. It was a little risqué, being so short, but I loved it the second I put it on.

"Nothing, you just look... Wow." He clears his throat. "I've never seen you dressed up like this."

"Thanks. Mum picked it all out for me today. James had some creative input too - He picked the belt. Who knew he had so much knowledge on women's clothes?" I say as I run my fingertips along the studded belt that makes my waist look tiny. Mum didn't agree but I thought it gave the outfit a little more edge, along with my brand-new Christian Louboutin boots and matching clutch. It's by far the most extravagant purchase I've ever made but the way I felt when I tried it on in the shop told me that I had to have the whole outfit.

And the new bottle of Gucci Guilty perfume…

And the red Dior lipstick…

It had been years since I bought anything nice to wear so I went all out.

The hostess shows us to our table and Jake pulls out my chair for me.

"That was very chivalrous, thank you," I say to Jake as the host lays down our menus and places crisp white napkins in our laps. She offers a smile to both me and Jake, informs us that our waiter will be over in just a moment and walks away, leaving us alone once again.

"Just because it's not a date doesn't mean I can't be charming. I told you, the point of this is for you to get to know the real me and for me to get to know you, again. And *this* is me. Although I am showing off slightly by getting us this reservation, I'll admit." His smile is infectious, the same genuine smile that you can't help but return.

"Okay, so this is amazing. Thank you," I say, looking around and taking it all in. "I can't believe you got us a table here at such short notice"

"Not going to lie, I'm slightly disappointed that Fred and Merlin don't actually work here," he casually states.

"You watch *'First Dates'*?"

"It's not usually my thing but I watched a couple of episodes this afternoon in preparation and now I think I might be addicted," he stage whispers, making me laugh out loud. "I'll probably watch another few episodes before bed, too."

The waiter takes our orders and brings us the fancy wine Jake chose. This is yet another side of him I've not seen before and it's making me question everything I thought I knew about him.

"Moving day on Monday. Are you excited?"

"You know, I'm not dreading it," I honestly say. If he had asked me that on Friday afternoon, I would have had a different answer but it's funny how much can change in 24 hours.

He smiles as though he knows this too. "I'm winning you over, aren't I?"

"Yeah, a little... You just seem to act so differently in the office."

"So do you. You're not as much of a control nut out in the human world."

"I don't think I'm too controlling," I say as he raises his eyebrows at me "Yeah, okay, I am but it's because of you! The way you waltz around, hypnotising my staff with your good looks and devil-may-care attitude, they honestly get nothing done. And, you have to admit, you love to torment me that way."

"You think I'm good looking then?" I just raise my eyebrows at him. "Sorry, flirting is my first line of defence."

Just like this morning, our conversation flows well. We talk mostly about generic things like our favourite TV shows, movies and food. A short while later, the waiter returns with our food and places two of the most perfectly cooked steaks I've ever seen in front of us.

"This is amazing. Do you treat all of your dates to this or do you save it for non-dates, like me?" I ask between bites.

"I haven't been on a date since I took Molly Anderson to see Tokyo Drift in sixth form."

"Oh, come on. You expect me to believe that?"

He shrugs slightly. "You want me to be honest?" I nod to him to continue. "I'm not the dating type. I meet girls in bars, the kind of girls who don't care when I leave when we're done, if you know what I mean."

For some reason, the thought of him meeting some random girl in a bar and shagging her makes my stomach turn.

"I know that makes me sound like a twat but it doesn't happen anywhere near as often as I'd have you believe. Yeah, I'm a flirt and have a big ego but I don't sleep around all that much," he says, looking down at his plate again, looking almost shy. "Just wanted you to know."

"Well, thank you for being honest. Tell me, is there a reason you don't take girls on dates?"

"Well, there was a time when I really liked someone, back when I was at uni, but she's never been available. I didn't want anyone as much as I wanted her so I stopped pining for Mrs Right and started looking for Mrs Right Now."

"Did you love her?"

"Yeah, I've never stopped. Don't think I ever will." His honesty catches me off guard and I feel for him. I know what it's like, wanting someone so desperately and knowing you'll never have them.

"I'm sure that, one day, you'll find someone special. Forget that girl, she's an idiot. You can't keep waiting around for a person who is never going to be available. As much as it pains me to say, you're a decent man, when you want to be. You deserve to fall in love and have them love you back."

Something I said makes him laugh. "What about you, do you date much? Unlike me, you don't broadcast your sex life around the place."

"The last person I went on a date with was Philip."

"Seriously?"

I nod, feeling suddenly embarrassed. Compared to his dating history, I may as well be locked away in a convent.

"That's a long time to be alone."

"Yeah but, at the same time, it feels just like yesterday when he died."

"You're not wearing your wedding rings anymore," he points out. I didn't even think he would notice if I still wore them. "I noticed when you held my hand last night but didn't want to pry."

"Yeah, took them off when I got home after Mum's New Year party. I have a standing phone appointment with my therapist on New Year's Day. I promised her the year before that I would take them off before our next appointment," I say, looking at the indent on my empty ring finger. "I turned 30. New decade, promotion, fresh start, if that's what I can call it."

"He'd be so proud of you."

"He'd be proud of both of us, taking this on together. He always believed in you, even when I didn't. He knew that this would happen, that we would have to work together and that our differences would need to be resolved. Whenever he talked about you, it was like he knew something I didn't. Maybe this was it."

"I'm not convinced I deserve his pride, especially after the way I've treated you the past decade," he admits.

"Neither of us are innocent in this. We've both acted poorly over the years but, like I said, this can be a fresh start. I want to start as we mean to go on, as friends as well as colleagues."

"I'll cheers to that," he says, raising his glass to meet mine. "To our fresh start because, as long as we have each other, we'll never be alone."

***

After we finish our meals, we are suitably stuffed but neither of us seem to be ready to call it a night.

We find a small table with a soft sofa in a late-night bistro we come across on a side street. We order two glasses of red wine and the wood burner in the corner blasts out heat that fills the entire room while smooth Jazz plays over the speaker system. Our table is tucked away in a corner and it feels like it could just be the two of us here, our bodies turned in towards each other, illuminated by the candlelight.

"Thank you for tonight. I've had a lovely non-date."

"Me too," he says, settling in next to me on the sofa as I sit facing him with one leg tucked under myself. "Do you still think I'm a shithead?"

"I'm sorry I called you that. At the time, I thought it was justified, even if it is the most immature name I've ever called anyone."

"I like it," Jake says with a laugh. "It's a great insult."

"I have to admit, you surprised me at how much of a non-shithead you can be," I say, making him laugh again.

"I told you that, if you got to know me again, you'd feel differently about me."

We sit in a comfortable silence for a few minutes. There is something I've wanted to ask him, something I've been too scared to know the answer to but I figure that, while we're here, with our guards down, I've got nothing to lose.

"Why did we stop being friends?" I ask, the curiosity getting the better of me. "We were all so close and then it changed. You stopped speaking to me pretty much overnight. Laura and Philip, too."

Surprise briefly flashes across his face. He wasn't expecting me to ask that and I don't think he is ready to answer either. My fingers are aching with the need to tap on the back of the sofa where my hand rests but I don't let them.

He thinks for a second. "When I was at uni, I got a lot of new attention. I thought I was better than I was and just kind of left you all behind. You should know, I've made some mistakes in my life but that's one of the few I regret." I'm not sure I believe the reason why but I don't push him on it.

"Why did you leave your party early the other night?" I should have seen it coming; I asked him a tough question so he asks me a tougher one.

"That day is hard for me. I don't enjoy the parties but I do it for Mum and Dad and Dave and Angie. They're his parents and they want to celebrate Philip's life but all I want to do is stay home and cry on my own. It's pathetic, I know. I torture myself every year and try to remember that night but I can't. I don't even remember the flight into London or collecting our bags when we landed. I don't remember how we felt. Were we tired from travelling? Excited to see our families? I don't even know what the last conversation we had was," the words spill out as Jake sits and listens intently. "People have told me bits and pieces. I've seen pictures of the wreckage but I've got no memories of my own. I just remember waking up in hospital with James while everyone else was at my husband's funeral."

He holds my hand gently; such a small act from him is so comforting and the urge to tap my fingers evaporates.

"Sorry, that was a much too emotional response to your question."

"I was there, too, you know, with James when you woke up. I ran out to get the nurse but, because I wasn't family, they wouldn't let me back in the room when they were seeing to you."

"I didn't know," I say, trying to remember that little room from eight years ago. I don't remember seeing Jake at all. All I remember is my brother, ashen faced and standing in the corner while medical staff peppered me with questions. I remember being overwhelmed by beeping machines all around me and the urge to rip the multiple tubes out of my veins.

He shrugs. "I don't like to talk about it. It was difficult seeing you and Philip like that. I thought that, if you knew how involved I was when you were in hospital, you might ask me questions that I don't have answers to."

"This is not how I expected this night to go," I say, laughing so I don't start crying. "Don't worry, I won't push for answers. If you ever want to talk to me about it, I'd like to hear what you have to say."

"One day, I'll tell you about it but I'm supposed to be impressing you tonight, not bringing the mood down."

"I'm glad you told me. Thank you," I say with a smile. "Let's change the subject so we don't start crying."

I didn't expect this reaction from him. Seeing him get emotional when talking about the accident revealed yet another layer of Jake and I'm beginning to wonder how many layers he has and how many he's willing to show me.

CHAPTER FOUR

The greatest thing about your best friend being an incredible baker is getting to taste test any new creations before they go on the menu. Even when we were kids, Laura would bake cakes and desserts for us to try out and she was always mixing new flavour combinations or perfecting her decorating skills.

After she completed her studies at Le Cordon Bleu, she moved to Paris to work with a famous French Pastry Chef but, after a bad break-up and the death of her brother, she moved back to London.

She opened her bakery, Laura's Kitchen, after turning down Pastry Chef positions at some of the most prestigious hotels in London. Everyone thought she was crazy to turn down those opportunities but I understood why she did. She wanted to be her own boss and make her own rules. She knew the pressures of working under famous chefs, the gruelling work hours for little appreciation and she didn't want that again. She wanted to love going into work and for her craft to be accessed by everyone, not just the wealthy or famous.

The display cases in the cafe boast mountains of Baklava, Stroop Waffles, sweet and savoury Empanadas to name a few. It's not just world food you can find here; there is a wide variety of traditional English bakes, including my favourite Battenburg and Bakewell Tarts.

Harry and I sit on tall stools at the end of the counter, patiently waiting for her next American pancake creation. People travel from all over the city to try them while many other cafes try to replicate them but fail. Laura is the only one who knows the secret ingredient in her pancake batter, after all.

"This one is salted caramel Biscoff. People are going mad for Lotus Biscoff now. Buttermilk pancakes, a Biscoff and salted caramel sauce with crumbled Lotus biscuits and fudge chunks on top," she details as Harry and I sit, fascinated by the plate in front of us. My stomach grumbles just looking at it. I quickly snap a photo because I know Jake would appreciate it. "This one is bacon and sausage covered in actual Canadian Maple syrup that was sent to me from a friend who lives in Toronto."

Harry and I exchange a look of trepidation at this one. "Just try it before you pass judgement," Laura scolds us.

We decide to try the weird one first, get it over with. "This is a taste sensation," Harry says, enthusiastically shovelling more of it in his mouth. I nod in agreement as I chew through my mouth full. The sweet syrup blends perfectly together with the smoky bacon and herb infused sausages.

"I think this might be my new favourite," I say.

I send the pictures to Jake as the three of us eat in silence, a good sign of food being enjoyed.

"So, Harry, I'm surprised you managed to tear yourself away from Simon today."

"I promised Laura I would be here so here I am. Plus, Simon had to work today. I'll see him later. We're going on our first date."

"I thought you hung out last night?" I ask.

"A weekend at home having sex doesn't count as a date, does it, Harry?" Laura explains, rolling her eyes at me as Harry agrees.

"Hey, I'm rusty with this whole dating thing."

"I think I might be in love," Harry declares. "Honestly, I think he's the one." The thing with Harry is that he falls in love just as quick as he falls out of it.

My phone vibrates with a new message and I smile when I see Jake's name on the screen.

Jake: Ah man, that looks incredible... Save me some?

Maggie: Too late. I'll think about bringing you a treat to work tomorrow.

"Jake?" Laura asks as she and Harry wear matching grins.

"He said the pancakes look incredible and he wants some," I say, putting my phone down as they share a look.

"Are you going to tell us about last night then? Harry and I are dying to hear the goss."

"It was great. The restaurant was amazing, we had a walk

around Covent Garden and then had a few drinks in a bistro by the Jubilee Market. We literally talked for hours, it felt like old times," I say as I fondly remember our night.

"Did he kiss you?" Harry asks.

"No, of course not. It wasn't a date." I think for a second before asking Laura the question that's been bouncing around my brain since Jake mentioned it last night. "Did you know he was in the hospital when I woke up from the coma?"

It's the first time I've asked her about the hospital. We sometimes talk about Philip but we have never spoken about the accident or the time I spent in hospital.

"Yeah. Did you not?"

"No, not until he mentioned something about it last night."

"He and James would come and sit with you every day for an hour or two so your parents could have a break and get something to eat. James was scared of being alone with you in case something happened so Jake came with him. I wonder why he never mentioned it to you before."

"He said he finds it really hard to talk about."

"That's understandable. From what I know, he and Philip were still close, even if he wasn't that close to you and me."

"So, if last night wasn't a date, have you had any hits from your dating apps?" Harry asks.

"Is it normal for men to send you unsolicited pictures of their penis?"

"Yes," they both agree. "Men think it's a sure-fire way into a girl's pants when it has the complete opposite effect. It's called a dick pic," Laura continues.

"Well, I have twenty-three dick pics in my Tinder inbox that I would desperately like to unsee." I shudder for dramatic impact.

"Show me!" Harry excitedly bounces on his chair, holding his hand out for my phone. "If men didn't want their junk to be scrutinised, they wouldn't send you a picture."

I hand over my phone and sit, sipping my coffee. It doesn't take long until we're in fits of laughter.

"Keep at it, Maggie. You'll find a tiny diamond in the rough, eventually," Laura says, smiling as she hands back my phone.

"Yeah, I hope so."

***

Jake appears at my desk bright eyed and bushy tailed early on Monday morning, armed with my usual coffee order. I check my watch to make sure I've got the time right.

"Don't look too surprised, Maggs," he says, puffing his chest out proudly at the fact he's early.

"You're an hour early for work!" I say, standing to place my hand over his forehead checking his temperature. "Are you sick?"

"Har-har. You're hilarious, did you know that?"

"Cloned?"

"Are you done?"

"I know... Abducted by aliens," I say, laughing way too hard at my own jokes. "Okay, okay, I'm done."

"Get your shit, you're with me today," he says, grinning.

I pick up my laptop, mobile and note pad before I hurry to follow him out the door as he takes long strides ahead of me, forgetting my little legs are half the length of his. He realises and slows down to match my pace as we reach the stairs.

"I haven't told them you're coming today. I thought it might help to see what we do without giving them time to freak out about it. You're a pretty big deal down here," he says as we step out of the stairwell and onto the Creative floor.

"What do you mean a 'pretty big deal'?"

"How long is it going to take for you to really see yourself?" he says, rolling his eyes.

I don't know what to say to that so I just shrug my shoulders.

"All the girls want to be you and the blokes want to..." He thinks for a second. "The blokes want to make you smile," he says triumphantly, impressed that he managed to keep his remark clean. "At the last count, sixty three percent of my staff are women. Many of them quite young, below thirty, super talented, too. Maggs, you're an inspiration to these women, women coming in from uni or from other agencies that aren't as 'gender inclusive', shall we say. They see you, a strong yet compassionate woman in leadership, and they look up to you."

The main insecurity I have in my position is my gender not because I don't love being a woman in leadership but because, all in all, it's still quite rare. If I can inspire even just one girl to give it a go, I'd be happy.

When we walk into the open plan office, everyone stops what they are doing to stare at us. It dawns on me how little effort I've put into coming down here over the years. In fact, I don't think I've been down here since I started avoiding Jake. If I need to speak to someone down here, I usually send an email or get Sasha to ask them to come see me.

"Right, ladies and gents. Maggie is going to be spending the day down here with us so please try to not make me look like a complete shithead," he smirks. I called him a shithead one time and he's never going to drop it.

People start returning to their work as Jake leads me around the floor, pointing out banks of desks, explaining where different teams sit and what they do.

It takes around an hour for him to introduce me to everyone one by one and I'm fascinated to discover he knows everyone's name, even the young interns he stops to chat to. He's confident and professional, the ego he usually displays is nowhere to be seen down here. Then, it hits me: Down here, he's comfortable and he doesn't need to overcompensate. Unlike when he would come up to my floor and I would purposely make him uncomfortable in the hope that it would keep him away.

Now, I feel like the shithead.

"How do you remember everyone's names?" I ask when we finally reach his office at the far end of the room. "There has to be a hundred people out there."

"I asked the same thing of my boss, too, when I started working here. He put it simply: If they know my name, I should know theirs. It stuck with me so I made it a priority to learn everyone's name and try to remember something about them. If you ask me, I'd say that a small act of remembering their names will bring in bigger rewards. For example, they work harder because they feel valued; if they feel valued by their boss remembering their names, they're more likely to stick around. If you look at my staff retention rate, you'll see it's rather high."

I'm speechless. It just goes to show that there are so many sides to him. There's my brother's boisterous best friend, the arrogant womanizer I thought I knew and the chivalrous gentleman who took me to dinner at a posh restaurant and treated me like a princess. Then there's this version of Jake I'm seeing for the first time, the amazing man his staff know and love. It's clear they love what they do, they love working for him. There is such a buzz when he walks around, when he stops to chat to people, when he asks about plans they had at the weekend or looks at their work.

In the last four days, I've come to see him in an entirely new light and it's taken me completely by surprise.

It also surprises me to see that there is absolutely no

flirting from him down here. Even when one of his extremely attractive, young graphic designers comes to talk to him in her tight jeans and figure-hugging shirt, he doesn't even seem to acknowledge the fact that she is beautiful. He speaks to her like his equal, not like the usual way I see him interact with gorgeous women.

I walk through the office as he talks to Thomas and look around. I'm not surprised to see a picture on his desk of him, his parents and grandparents at his graduation. He was always so close to his grandparents and they were all so proud of him. It was heart-breaking when they died in quick succession of each other and James told me it hit him hard.

I stop to admire the work on the walls. There are drawings and ideas plastered over most of the available surfaces, white boards full of brainstorms, jokes and copy ideas. Everything is so visual and bright. There's work I recognise from campaigns we've completed, other work which I know is ongoing and new things, doodles and ideas just waiting to take off.

It's like he knows what I'm thinking as he comes to stand next to me, pulling an A3 portfolio from the shelves.

"You see things as numbers and graphs, SWOT analysis and SMART goals. *This* is what I see. Brainstorms, sketches and storyboards." He opens the folder to show me the work inside.

"You're responsible for all these?" I ask, looking through the pages in awe.

"Well, it was a team effort," he says, looking slightly

nervous, as if he's waiting for me to judge his work.

"They were all him. I know it's hard to believe but this dude is modest. Everything you see there came from this brain here," a hipster looking guy says as he teases Jake's hair. He's wearing the skinniest jeans I've ever seen and a beanie with giant holes in it that hangs off the back of his head. Surely it can't be very practical for wintry weather?

Jake rolls his eyes as he fixes his tousled hair.

"Maggie, this is Jude," he says, introducing us as Jude sticks his thin hand out to shake mine. "Jude is on our social media team. He's just been promoted, actually, to Head of Social so you might have spoken to him"

"Jude Spencer? It's nice to put a face to the email signature," I say, acknowledging that I have spoken to him.

"Likewise," Jude laughs. "You know, I can't blame him for leaving us when he's going to be sharing an office with such a beautiful lady, like yourself. Intelligent, too, from what I hear. You're the only person in the world that makes Jake Mills sweat, did you know that?"

I look at Jake with raised eyebrows and a slightly smug smile. "I did not know that, tell me more!"

Jude continues with a diabolical smile in Jake's direction. "He makes the shittest excuses to go and skive upstairs. He gets all giddy and excited and he *always* comes back in a good mood."

"Okay, that's enough of that," Jake says, quickly interrupting Jude and ruining my fun.

They chat for a moment about a campaign they've been working on so I keep myself occupied by flipping through his portfolio, still smiling at the snippets of Jake revealed by Jude. I had no idea he was so talented. I knew he was good at his job, you just need to see the results he pulls in to know that, but I didn't know he could do all of this.

As I near the end of the book, I reach the personal stuff. I should probably stop looking but I don't. I'm taken aback by the portraits he's drawn. There are dozens of perfectly sketched pictures. There's an intricate sketch of his childhood home, each pencil mark placed exactly where it needs to be to capture its essence. There are beautiful hand drawn pictures of his parents and grandparents, a few of my mum and dad as well as James, Laura and others I don't know.

There is one of me too.

I recognise myself from a picture hanging in Mum and Dad's living room. I can't remember who took it but I know it's from the night I got engaged. I'm so young in this picture and I look incredibly happy. Seeing this drawing brings back the memories of that night, the love I felt. It brings back the excitement I had for the future when Philip, as nervous as he was, got down on one knee in front of our loved ones and asked me to spend the rest of my life with him. If only this girl knew the heartache that was to come, what life had in store for her.

I turn the page and my heart stops when I see the handsome face looking back at me. Philip's almond eyes stare up from the page in front of me, his full lips pulled in a wide grin. I can feel his cheeky demeanour shining from the page. It's so incredibly lifelike, perfect.

I run my fingers down the plastic cover protecting the drawing as emotion tries to take hold of me.

"So, Maggie, I'm glad you're both here because I actually wanted to talk to you both about something," Jude says, reminding me that he's here. I take a second to close the folder and get my shit together before I turn to face them.

"Sure," I say, taking a seat opposite Jake as he looks at me intensely. He knows what I saw. Jude doesn't seem to notice the shift in my mood.

"Well, since the news is being announced next week that you both are taking over the company, I thought it would be good to get you guys on our social so people can get an insight to what you do on a day-to-day basis. It would really help to create a genuine relationship with our followers."

"Will people even care about what we do daily?" Jake asks.

"Totally. People love seeing behind the scenes stuff and this is the perfect opportunity to expand our repertoire," he says dramatically.

"Sure," I say "It'll help appeal to a younger market. A lot of new companies are set up by the younger generations so maybe that's an effective way to target them. You should speak to Lou in Web Design. Maybe link up the existing website and blog content so it's consistent with social."

"Speak to Thomas and Sasha, arrange a meeting with everyone for next week once you've all had chance to speak and get some content ideas down. We'll go from there."

"That's great. I'll start working on it right away." Jude pauses as he reaches the door to leave. "Before I go, are you coming to the King's Arms tonight? That barmaid missed you on Friday. She was asking after you again."

"Not tonight, I've got plans"

The plans he is referring to is moving into our new office, something that I expected him to do during working hours but he insisted that we get a takeaway and bottle of wine. He'd suggested we do it after everyone has gone home for the day so we can get it sorted with no interruptions and, since I'm enjoying his company much more than I thought I would, I'm desperate to know more about him.

"Hot date, huh?" Jude says, laughing.

"Something like that," he says, flashing a smile my way which makes my cheeks burn.

***

Once everyone has left for the day, we start on the office move and it doesn't take too long before our office starts coming together. IT had already set up our computers and phones earlier this afternoon so all we had to do was connect our laptops and we were good to go with our technology.

We didn't think in advance about how we were going to move the countless books and files we have accumulated over the years, even though I was usually very pragmatic. Luckily, Jake has exceptional upper body strength and managed to lug all our boxes up two flights of stairs to our new floor.

Me? Well, I got to direct him, make sure he didn't trip, things like that. It wasn't an excuse to watch him use his muscles or anything, that was just a bonus.

The items which were too heavy to lift will need to be brought up another day but there is plenty of work for us to do with what we have.

The space we're moving to is much bigger than the floors we previously worked on and there's even enough room to have all our staff on the same floor for once. Jake had excitedly suggested the idea, claiming that 'if we bring our teams together, not just management, we can increase productivity. They can get to know each other and where their strengths lie'. I had to agree with him; it is a great idea and there is more than enough room. Surprisingly, when we pitched it to everyone late this afternoon after the Stephenson's Chocolate meeting, they were all excited. I thought one or two people might complain but no one did. I suppose there's something exciting about change, a new challenge, almost. New friends to be made and experiences to be had.

Working with Jake today was really refreshing too. Getting to see his processes was interesting and I loved meeting people I had heard so much about from him already. I enjoyed the day much more that I imagined I ever would.

It gave me a better insight into myself too.

I've given him such a tough time about how he's treated me that I didn't realise how badly I have been treating him this whole time, too. There were lots of things that I should have noticed earlier, like why hadn't I noticed how passionate he is? Or how incredibly talented he is? It's the first time I've seen him as a leader, someone who inspires and motivates his staff and I'm ashamed to admit that I completely underestimated his abilities. Watching him interact with his staff highlighted how different our leadership styles are and how I can learn from having him around.

"You're going to regret the glass," Jake says, sitting cross legged on the floor next to me as I help him stack his uni text books alongside mine. The long bookcase that sits below our window is bulging with thousands of pounds worth of textbooks that were hardly used at uni and haven't been opened since we graduated, yet neither of us can bear to part with them.

"And why is that?" I ask.

"Because you can't hide from people when they're looking for you to do shit you don't want to do."

"We're in charge now, Jake. It doesn't matter if we don't want to do shit, we have to do it anyway."

"It's called delegating, Maggs. You should try it sometime, instead of shouldering the burden," he says, getting to his feet to fetch the wine bottle from my desk and joining me again on the floor.

"I know how to delegate," I say although it doesn't mean I'm particularly good at practicing what I preach. "Besides, it sends a good message to be accessible. I want people to see us as approachable," I say, taking in the large wall of glass with a set of double doors in the centre that separate our office from the main floor.

Jake empties the rest of the bottle into my mug, not making any attempt to argue his point.

"You're a bad influence on me already, Mr Mills. I don't usually drink on a school night."

"Think of it like this: You're a good influence on me so it evens itself out. Plus, we're drinking out of coffee mugs so we can pretend it's just coffee," he says, a mischievous smile tugs at his lips as he looks over his mug at me.

"In that case, let's cheers to our new home away from home," I say, clinking my cup to his.

"I'm sorry I didn't pre-warn you about the sketches," he says out of the blue. "I forgot they we're in there. I haven't looked at them for a long time."

"They we're beautiful, Jake. I had no idea you could draw like that"

"I haven't drawn for a while. I used to a lot. It's embarrassing how many pictures I've drawn of you all."

"I'd love to see more."

We sit on the floor, surrounded by boxes, for the next hour

as we look through his sketches. There are more of his family and James, Laura and Philip, some based on photographs and some from memory. There are people I don't recognise at all and there are none of me. I can't help but wonder why.

"I'm not in here."

"Please don't think this is weird or creepy," he says as he reluctantly hands me a smaller A4 folder.

I take it from him and turn the pages. There are at least a dozen drawings in here, all of me.

"These are unfinished. I liked drawing you but I could never get it exactly right. There was always something missing," he says, looking through at the pages with me. I notice I look prettier in his drawings than I do in real life.

"This book was the hardest to draw. It might be difficult for you to see," he says, warning me before flicking through another sketchbook. He looks at it for a second, his ice blue eyes shining with emotion before he hands it to me. "I drew these in the hospital. James and I would spend hours a night with you. We came together because we were so scared to come alone, in case something happened to you. We'd always bring snacks, three of anything we thought you would like. Cake, crisps, chocolate. We would hold it under your nose to try and wake you up. When that didn't work, we would describe it to you in intense details as we ate whatever it was. Taste, texture, smell. It never worked but we still kept it up because we were willing to try anything to wake you up."

I look at the first drawing of Philip and me on our wedding day. It's beautiful. There are more like it, each one as stunning as the next, bringing tears to my eyes.

"You didn't come to the wedding." I say as I look at the pictures.

"Your mum showed me pictures. I wanted to draw one for her but, like I said, they weren't perfect."

I stop when I come to the last picture in the book; it's another one of me but, instead of it being a happy memory, it's me in my hospital bed with my eyes closed. There is another person, drawn a few shades lighter than the rest of the picture, sat in the chair next to me. It's Philip.

"Maggie, I'm so sorry. I didn't mean to upset you," Jake says as the tears I am usually so good at controlling spill down my cheeks.

His arms are around me in a second, holding me tighter than ever before, comforting me like it's second nature for him. He doesn't speak as I sob into his chest, clinging onto his soft hoodie so tight that my fingertips turn white. He pulls me closer so I'm sat in his lap on the floor while he trails patterns on my back with his fingertips, stroking away my pain.

Eventually, I stop crying but I don't let go of him. I stay where I am, needing his strength to pull myself together again. This must be what my therapist meant when she warned me about my compartmentalising. Without warning, the box containing my grief flew open and spread its contents all over the floor for Jake to see.

"Thank you for showing me," I say, eventually, my voice still shaking slightly. "They're really beautiful. You're so talented."

I take one last look at the picture before I close the book and hand it back to Jake. I climb out of his embrace and dab my eyes with the sleeve of my jumper.

"Sorry for the slight breakdown," I say, unable to meet his eyes. "I didn't know it but I really needed that cry."

I excuse myself, leaving Jake to put away his sketch books and folders while I take myself to the loo so I can attempt to make myself look somewhat presentable again.

Despite Jake probably thinking I'm completely unstable, I take this as another win, another surprising insight into the man I thought I knew so well.

***

It's close to midnight when we finally finish unpacking our boxes. It took longer than anticipated due to the amount of laughing and carrying on we did when we opened the second bottle of wine after my emotional outburst.

It reminded me of being at uni when me, Philip, Laura and Harry would insist on working on an assignment late at night because we were sure to be more productive at that time. Instead, we'd end up playing with the green screen in the computer suite, pretending to be under water or on a roller coaster. We'd drink can after can of cheap, home brand energy drinks, eating food that wasn't good for us and spend hours swinging around on swivel chairs until our faces hurt from laughing so much.

When Jake and I finally decide it's best to go home for the evening and get a few hours' sleep, we take a moment to ourselves and stand in the doorway. His arm sits around my shoulder while I wrap both arms around his waist, holding on tightly and taking it all in. The large, open workspace is ready and waiting for our excited teams as is our own beautiful, shiny office. On the left is my desk, meticulously organised with my ergonomic chair and rows upon rows of filing cabinets, each organised alphabetically and colour coded.

On the right is Jake's desk. For the moment, it's neat and tidy but even he doesn't expect that to last long. 'Organised chaos', he likes to call it. His beat-up, old drawing table that his dad bought him as a graduation present stands in the corner next to the white boards that he had brought up from his old office.

It's as if two worlds that have no business being together have collided, trivial things that don't usually exist together, co-existing perfectly. Almost like the two of us.

"I don't know about you but I can't wait to come in to work tomorrow," he says, pulling me in tighter and kissing the top of my head, an action which feels so natural now. I can't help but beam up at him.

"Our Uber is here," I say as the app pings in my pocket. I

don't make any attempt to move from his warm embrace. Where I would usually insist on making a fast dash so as not to make the driver wait any longer than necessary, I choose to enjoy the moment with Jake and it seems like he had the same idea too.

CHAPTER FIVE

The first week in our new office went by in the blink of an eye. As well as spending the week learning the ropes, we also had to fit in work on our other projects which hasn't left much time for anything else. Dad and Ray finished up, officially leaving me and Jake in charge as of 5 pm Thursday. It was a daunting prospect to face.

"It's the end of one era and the beginning of another," Dad had said as they joined us in our office, holding a rather expensive bottle of champagne. "Don't be afraid to take risks or make mistakes. It's all part of learning."

"And look after each other," Ray added before proposing a toast. "Here's to you both enjoying the same, if not more, success than we did."

I was sad when they walked out of the building for the last time. I had learnt so much from them over the years and owed them so much more. I saw their smiling faces as they left to start their new, more relaxed lives and I was glad that they were still best friends after 40 years of working together. One day, I hoped to see Jake and I do the same, knowing we'd made the right choices and took the right path together.

Each day this week, a new group of people had joined us in our new, top floor office and their faces always expressed the same emotions. There was excitement over mixing with their colleagues that they usually wouldn't see, wonder as they looked out of the glass wall overlooking the Thames. From this level, you can see for miles across London and it really is a remarkable sight, even in the gloomy January rain. Natural light floods the room, resulting in a feeling that I can only describe as fresh and freeing.

There is a palpable buzz in the air that builds each day as more and more people join us. They bring new personalities to the mix as people meet for the first time despite working only one floor apart for who knows how long. It feels like how I imagine watching your children making new friends in the school yard feels like. There are nerves and excitement but, deep down, you know everything will be fine at the end of the day.

This is the fresh start I was hoping for and, for the first time, I feel optimistic for the future. I can see past the grief and see my life progressing naturally.

Jake and I are closer than ever before, it's almost like the last eight years hadn't happened at all. My friendship with him is different to how it is with everyone else. I haven't had the pressure of putting on a show or having to *pretend* like I'm having a good time because I *am* having the best time with him. We can act as ridiculous as we want and that's okay because, unlike everyone else, he isn't watching me 24 hours a day, waiting for me to slip up and admit to how hard life has been living as a widow in her twenties. It probably had something to do with my emotional breakdown on Monday: He saw, first-hand, how damaged I am and there was no reason to feel embarrassed about it.

He hasn't brought up what happened the other night and neither have I but, if I had wanted to talk about it, I know that he'd be there to talk to.

I think back to how I've behaved over the years, hiding my emotions and my pain. With Jake, I can't hide it and I don't want to hide it. I have the urge to tell him everything. No-one has ever been able to comfort me like he did. No-one has ever held me quite like he did. I wonder if he realises how much he's helped me this past week, breathing fresh air into my life like a breeze blowing away the dust that's settled on me over time.

I wonder if he knew what it was like before he opened his life back up to me. Has James told him the extent of my low moods over the years? Did he talk to him how broken I've been and still am?

I'm not quite clinically depressed (as much as my therapist thought I was) but I'm certainly not happy. At least, I wasn't happy for a while. Lost would be a better description; not knowing where I fit in without Philip, having no idea about the kind of person I used to be, never mind the person I want to be.

I love talking to Jake. Whenever we aren't at work, we're texting each other about absolutely anything. If he sees something on Facebook that he thinks I'll like or find funny, he sends it to me. He knows that I still don't have an account, no matter how much he tells me I'm living in the stone age.

We take it in turns to buy our morning coffees – he bought today's. He's gone as far as sharing the biscuits his mum baked for him despite me knowing he never shares them. We've eaten dinner together almost every night this week, too. Since we've been putting in extra hours on the Stephenson's pitch, we either order a takeaway to the office or eat in the restaurant below our building if we need to take a step back from our work.

I smile as I look over to him, sat at his desk, wearing a dark jumper over an open collared shirt and dark jeans - a far cry from what he used to wear to work. When I asked him why he opts for a shirt instead of a t-shirt now, he'd told me that he wanted to make an effort for his new position.

I can tell he's concentrating hard on whatever he is working on because, every so often, he moves his head to the side and chews on his lower lip. I have only ever seen him do this when he is working on his computer, never when he's writing on the white boards or working on his drawing table.

"What?" he asks with a grin as he catches me staring at him.

"Nothing. I was daydreaming," I say, blushing.

I avert my eyes and focus on my screen again but reread the same line of my email that I've been writing for twenty minutes.

Our phones buzz in quick succession. Laura set up a group chat the other night so I assume it's someone messaging both of us there. I give my head a quick shake and finish typing up the email I was working on before I pick up my phone to read the messages.

> Laura: George tonight?
> James: Yep.
> Simon: We'll be there at 8.
> Harry: I love how we're a 'we' now xoxoxox
> Helen: Can I bring Cylvie?

I can feel Jake watching me as I type and it takes all my self-control not to look up and meet his gaze. We had already agreed that we wouldn't work late on a Friday, that we would have everything finished by 5 so we could go to the pub. It was Jake's idea; he'd said that I put too many hours in as it is and I should enjoy a stress-free Friday night with my friends.

I quickly finish my text and put my phone face down, not meeting his eye.

> Maggie: Sorry, can't make it.

"You're not coming tonight?" Jake asks, looking at his phone. "Please don't say it's because of Cylvie?"

"No. I, uh, have plans," I say, vaguely waving it off, not really wanting to get into details.

"You got a date or something?" he says with a laugh as if it's a completely inconceivable idea.

"Yeah. Someone I met on this app Laura set me up on. It's no big deal," I say, trying to make it sound less daunting than it is.

I feel bad that I didn't mention it to him before now. I made a point of keeping it from him for no other reason than my request of him. He has stuck to his side of the bargain and hasn't mentioned his sex life to me at all this week so I didn't want to be a hypocrite and start talking about my new dating life.

I was about to give up on the whole online dating thing when Martin messaged me. It was a pleasant change from the dozens of dick pics I'd received over the course of the week. I mean, who even thinks that's okay?

Spoiler alert: It's not ever okay.

"Tell me it's not Tinder," he says through gritted teeth and a tense jaw. He sounds annoyed. Maybe I should have told him what's been going on in that aspect of my life.

"What if it is?" My instinct is to go on the defence. Why shouldn't I date? Why shouldn't I have a Tinder profile? Who does he think he is to judge me about my dating methods when all he does is go to the closest bar and finds the sluttiest girl? As soon as the thought enters my head, I get a horrible feeling that maybe he's been doing that and not telling me. Not that it bothers me; he can do what he wants.

"Come on, Maggs, you're worth more than a Tinder date."

"Just because I met the guy on Tinder doesn't mean he's not a decent person," I argue.

"Do you even know anything about him? How long have

you been speaking to him? What does he do for a living? Where does he live?" he says, shooting off questions.

"A few days. His name is Martin, he lives in Waterloo and he is an entrepreneur. Not really sure what sector but I'm sure I'll find out later when we get to know each other," I snap, letting my annoyance show. I hope he doesn't pry further because I know nothing else about this man other than what's on his profile.

"I think it's a terrible idea but whatever. Have fun," he says, standing to pack his things away and turning to leave. Not once has he left the office before me this week. He usually waits for me to finish up and we get the tube home together but, this time, he doesn't.

I don't want him to leave. I want him to stay and tell me why we're arguing about this on our first official day of being in charge. I want him to tell me why he's mad at me because he *is* mad, right?

"I'll see you tomorrow then?" he asks as he pauses in our doorway, looking like he wants me to say something. I should ask him to stay, ask him to talk to me but, for some stupid reason, I don't.

Instead, I settle for a snide remark. "Yeah, if you're out of your mood by then."

I regret it as soon as the words leave my mouth and it almost looks like he is about to snap back at me but thinks better of it.

"I'll call you in the morning, Maggs," he says, clenching

his jaw, the anger rolling off him in waves. With that, he walks out, leaving me staring at the empty space where he stood with no clue how we got to this point.

"What was that about?" Sasha asks me from her desk that sits just outside of our door. Thomas looks just as confused.

"I have no idea," I say in annoyance.

I sit back at my desk to reply to the last of my emails but I can't concentrate anymore. I pick my phone up and call him but his phone goes to voicemail, presumably because he is on the tube with no signal. When I try again half an hour later, he doesn't answer and I know he's purposely ignoring me. His phone is connected to his watch so I know he can see my call coming through. This time, he's choosing to ignore me and it annoys me more than it has any right to.

***

Martin arranges to meet me at a fancy restaurant in Chelsea so I wear a black, low cut dress that wraps around and pulls my waist in. I pair it with my new Louboutin's which now remind me of Jake. I try to focus on the positives rather than our earlier argument: I'm getting use out of my obscenely expensive shoes so it almost makes the cost worth it. I can't argue with how confident and sexy I feel in them.

The decor of the restaurant is sort of industrial chic with exposed brickwork that seems to be all the rage these days, brass accessories and weird, erotic art.

"My name is Tiff and I am your waitress this evening. Can I get you a drink?" the pretty waitress asks me.

"Glass of rosé, please," I ask.

"You seem nervous. First date?"

"You're good. It's my first date since my husband died eight years ago," I casually state, taking the waitress by surprise. I sometimes forget that it's not common to be a thirty-year-old widow.

"Oh, I'm so sorry,"

"Thank you. I just figure it's time to move forward with my life so I'm giving the dating thing a try."

"Well, Hun, I'm a pro at first dates. I see enough of them in here. The good, the bad, the ugly. If you need me, just give me a wave."

I relax like she's said the perfect words. It's reassuring that I've got someone looking out for me tonight even if I didn't know I needed that.

As Tiff leaves to get my drink, I quickly pull out my phone. After Jake left the office and decided to ignore me, I calmed down enough to try talking to him again. I must have sent him at least 10 texts that have gone un-answered, asking if he's okay or if he's still pissed off at me. He could really work on his communication skills and I would normally point that out but I don't want to rock the boat any more than I apparently already have.

This time, when I look at my phone, I'm relieved to see his name blinking back at me. At least he's not ignoring me anymore, though he does seem to avoid answering my questions.

Jake: Just be careful tonight, please. Ring me if you need anything or when you get home safe. I don't care what time it is x

Jake: I'll be at the George x

Does it mean he wants me to meet him there? I do notice there was no apology but maybe he wants to apologise in person. Why can't he just use his bloody words and tell me what's wrong?

I don't have time to reply or worry about Jake's bad mood as Martin walks in, escorted to our table by Tiff who gives me a quick smile. I quickly put my phone back in my clutch bag. I'll text him back later, give him a taste of his own medicine, see how he likes being ignored. I'm not his mum, I don't have to mother him or pander to his mood swings. I try to do my usual compartmentalising and lock him in a box in my mind to deal with later but, for some reason, I can't. It's like I can feel him pecking away at my brain, that little message of concern still niggling at me.

Why is he mad at me?

"Mandy, lovely to meet you," Martin says, kissing me on both cheeks all while having one eye trained on our pretty waitress, looking her up and down.

Great. Even she notices and gives me a look as if to say, '*Is this bloke for real?*'

"It's Maggie. Nice to meet you, too," I say, taking my seat again and ignoring the fact he's just openly checked out another woman within five seconds of meeting me.

I'm not sure what I was expecting but it wasn't this. His shirt is dirty and creased and his trousers hang far too low for comfort. He's wearing a chunky, gold chain that looks like it came out of a mid-90s Argos catalogue and a hoop in his ear that looks infected.

I try not to judge - I really do - he just doesn't look like someone who is on a date. He looks like he's thrown on the first lot of clothes he could find and raced out of the door. Had he even checked out this restaurant when he suggested it because they have a dress code and I'm sure he's violating it.

"I'll have a San Miguel, double vodka Red Bull and 2 shots of Patron," he says to her. "Do you want anything?" he adds to me.

"I have a drink, thank you," I say, trying not to sound appalled at the number of drinks he's ordered at such an early stage in our date.

We start off with small talk although I'm trying my best not to appear distracted. He talks about how shitty the weather has been this week, how nice the restaurant is, the recent tube strikes. It's really generic stuff, nothing to write home about. The entire time he's talking, his eyes follow Tiff and the other waitresses around the room. He's literally watching their every move and isn't trying to hide it at all.

Tiff brings him his drinks with a scowl, obviously having noticed his wandering eyes. He takes it upon himself to grab her hand and licks his lips at her which freaks me out as much as it does her.

This is not going well at all.

It gets even worse when he doesn't waste any time downing both shots of Tequila and his vodka Red Bull. Tiff and I just look at each other in disbelief.

Now, I'm a bit rusty when it comes to dating but I know that's not how you act on a date when you're trying to impress someone.

"Remember, I'll be right here if you need anything," she says for my benefit, walking away and keeping her narrowed eyes on my date.

"So, Molly -"

"Uh, it's Maggie." Seriously? Twice he's got my name wrong and I've had to correct him.

"Right, Right. I just want to get this out there in the open because that's the kind of guy I am. I'm honest. I don't want kids anytime soon and I don't want to get married. I'm not after anything serious. I am not monogamous and I like to keep my options open so there will be other women. I'm not willing to change anything for anyone, not even you, sweetheart. If you like me, this is what you get."

"Uh, excuse me?" is all I can say. I'm absolutely floored. Is this guy for real or is this a sick prank? Is this 2003? Can I expect Ashton to pop up from behind the bar and yell 'Punk'd'?

"I'll be right back. Need the pisser." Charming. He makes his way to the toilets by passing another waitress, trying to grab her arse. Maybe I can just ditch him and pay the waitress for my drink on my way out. I can go find my friends and salvage my night.

I try to hold my groan in when I think about Jake. How do I avoid telling him that he was right about this? Of course, he was right. He's always bloody right. Ugh, I really don't want him to know that he was right.

I pull out my phone again and openly groan when I find the group chat has been lit up with questions on how my date is going.

No more texts from Jake.

Laura: Is he good looking?

James: Just remember, not all of us want a play by play of this date.

Helen: Ignore him, the rest of us want to know everything. EVERYTHING!!!

Harry: Remember... No sex on the first date but that doesn't mean you can't have other kinds of fun ;) If you need any tips, just ask!

James: This is the type of shit a brother shouldn't have to read about his baby sister.

Maggie: Date is going well. Will text later.

It's a lie but I just can't face the embarrassment of them knowing how awful this date is.

Tiff comes over to the table to check on me as it's been 5 minutes since Martin went into the loo. She's tells me they sent a waiter in to check on him and I tell her I need to leave as soon as physically possible so follow her to the hostess stand.

I really wish I had left 5 minutes ago when I first had the idea because the next few moments pass in a blur.

As I'm about to pay, six police officers dressed in tactical gear make their way through the restaurant into the men's toilets. They aren't there long when they emerge with Martin, hands cuffed behind his back as they escort him out of the restaurant. I'm no expert but I've seen enough movies to understand that the white powder covering most of his face is probably a class A drug.

"Are you Martin Sinclair's date?" an officer asks as he approaches me at the payment machine.

"Yeah, Maggie, Maggie Jones," I say with a mix of shock and confusion as Martin is escorted out.

"Miss Jones, I need you to come with me," the officer says as he detaches his handcuffs from his belt, taking my clutch and coat from my arms.

Oh, dear god.

"Are you arresting me?" I ask, my voice a few octaves higher than usual. For the first time, I notice everyone in the restaurant is staring at me.

"We just want to ask you some questions about your boyfriend," he says, cuffing my hands in front of me and leading me out to the police car parked in front of the restaurant.

I'm in too much shock to say anything. I don't understand what's happening and, to be perfectly honest, I'm terrified. I can't go to prison on the first day of being CEO. I can't go to bloody prison at all.

Martin is being forced into the back of squad car as the man who introduced himself as Police Constable Jordan stands me next to his car.

"Officer, I can help. I witnessed the whole thing," Tiff says, running towards me. "She didn't know him and, from the second he walked in, he was a complete dick head to her."

"How did you meet Mr Sinclair?" Police Constable Jordan asks me.

Suddenly, I find my voice and the words rush out all at once. "I met him on Tinder. My friend, Laura, who is also my dead husband's sister, thought it would be a clever idea to get myself back out there. You see, I was married to her brother and he was killed in a car accident eight years ago. This was my first date since I lost him. I had spoken to Martin for the past 3 days and he asked me out so I said 'yeah, what's the worst that can happen?'. I didn't think I would be standing here in cuffs." I wave my wrists around dramatically. "He seemed like a normal bloke until he turned up late, tried to feel up the waitresses, drank 2 shots and a double vodka. He told me that he wanted to shag multiple women and then disappeared into the loos for 10 minutes. I was leaving when you all came in. I should have left sooner."

The Constable just stands there, dumbstruck as he stares at me. What is with everyone staring, for Christ sake?

"It's true, Officer," Tiff helpfully adds. "You can put me down as a witness and we can get the CCTV so you can see for yourself. There's no audio but you can probably see the expressions on our faces at what an asshat he was being."

I'm momentarily distracted by Tiff's use of the phrase 'asshat'. Maybe I can use that on Jake, too.

I can't think about Jake right now. Why can't I shove him in that box?

"I lost my wife, too. Six years ago" the Officer says, his eyes softening towards me. He gently removes the cuffs and I just thank my lucky stars there was no one taking photos of us. "She was hit by a drunk driver at 29 years old. I've tried the whole Tinder thing and it was just awful. I didn't end up in handcuffs or anything but it turns out the girl I was talking to was a catfish. Said she was in trouble abroad and needed money to get home. Obviously, it went no further than that."

"Jake - my business partner and my friend - he warned me to stay off Tinder. He said it wasn't the place for a girl like me. Guess I have to go and tell him he was right."

"You're a beautiful girl, Miss Jones. You'll find someone great, you just have to look in the right places. Maybe your friend is right. Take it from me, Tinder is rarely a place you find Mr Right."

"Thanks," I say with a smile as PC Jordan gently pats my arm. He can't be much older than me but he feels much wiser.

Another Officer comes to take my details, which takes a while, and says they'll be in touch if they need me to go on record about the events of the evening. I agree and she says I can leave. I'm just thankful I'm not in cuffs anymore.

The restaurant owner was lovely about the whole thing. I guess he took pity on me as he told me not to worry about the bill and to go spend time with my friends and have a bloody good drink. He even offered a voucher so I can come back another time. I declined as I will not be returning ever again.

I sigh, knowing it is time to face the music. I should tell them and get it over with. They'll be expecting an update soon, anyway, and I could really do with that drink.

I pull out my phone as I stand outside the tube station, not checking the thirteen unread messages in our group chat. I can't deal with reading them. I did think about calling Jake. I wanted to call him and he told me to if I needed anything but I chicken out, dialling my brother instead.

CHAPTER SIX

I reluctantly push on the doors of The George to find Laura, Helen, Harry and Simon sat at our regular table. I can't see Jake anywhere but his coat is hung on the end of the booth so I know he's here somewhere, probably with James.

I throw my bag down on the table with a thud, yank off my jacket and take the empty spot next to Laura.

"Didn't go well then?" she asks, smirking.

When I called James and told him what happened, I asked him to let the others know so I wouldn't have to relive the embarrassment. All I can do in response to Laura's question is groan as I shut my eyes, hiding my face in my arms on the table. I knew I would have to face it so I might as well get it over with.

"Alright, Maggs?" Jake happily says as he sits down next to me. I can hear him grinning, loving every second of being right. "You look like you could use this." He slides a fresh pint of cider towards me.

I drink the pint in a few un-lady-like gulps to the utter dismay of my friends. Yeah, I needed that.

"Nice," Jake remarks as I return my head to the table and bang it against the wood, repeatedly trying my best not to burp after having the gassy drink.

"So... how did it go?" Harry asks, tentatively. "Do you want to talk about it?"

"I got arrested Harry, how do you think it went!?" My words are muffled as my head is still buried in my arms.

"Walk us through it," Jake says, pulling me to sit by my shoulders and rubbing his hand on my back before settling it on the nape of my neck. I relax against his warm touch. I needed that too.

"He downed a double vodka Red Bull and 2 shots of Tequila within 30 seconds of him turning up late. He couldn't stop staring at our waitress - who was lovely, by the way - then tried to grab another waitress' arse. He also advised me that I would never be able to change him and that he would be dating other women. And, if that wasn't the worst part, he then disappeared to the toilet for ages and came out in handcuffs, escorted by armed police with white powder all over his face. The police seemed extremely interested in me, too, thought I was in on *'it'*, whatever *'it'* was. I didn't ask. They only let me go when I told the policeman everything and he took pity on me because he's a widower, too, and got catfished on Tinder a few years ago," I say in one breath, trying not to leave anything out.

Everyone sits, listening to me in shock. Their mouths open as they struggle to find the words.

Finally, Jake opens his mouth to speak but I quickly interrupt him. "Don't say it," I warn, knowing where his thoughts are.

"But I did say it was a bad idea."

I can't argue with him. That is what he said to me. I groan and rest my head on his shoulder as he gently rubs my arm, trying to reassure me.

"You know, they say it takes 5 bad dates before you have a good one."

"Do they?" I ask him, not knowing if I can handle more dates like that.

"No, I made it up." He smirks.

"Asshat," I fire back at him which he returns with his best laugh. He liked it which makes me smile again. I'm happy he seems to be out of his bad mood.

"Pool table just opened up," James says as he and Jake stand again, making their way across to the pool table.

"Chin up, Maggs," Jake says, all joking aside and softly lifting my face with his index finger as he gives me his best smile.

"We're going to the bar. Do you want anything?" Harry asks, taking Simon's hand.

"Yeah, another pint, please."

"One for me, please," Helen says as Laura just shakes her empty glass at him with a grin.

"They are so adorable," Laura says as she stares dreamily at them. "Harry told me he thinks he's in love with Simon."

"That's quick, isn't it?" I ask.

"I knew the moment I met James that I was in love with

him," Helen says, shrugging. "It just took him a little longer to figure it out."

"Has Jake been okay tonight?" I ask, trying to sound casual but, by the look they gave each other, I think they might have a suspicion something is up between us.

"Ugh, no, he's been in the worst mood all night," Laura answers.

"He kept angry texting on his phone. We couldn't see who it was to but it was a long message and then he just deleted it, sent another message and slammed his phone down." Helen tucks her head down slightly, lowered her voice. "He and James went to sit at the bar for a while to talk. I think James knows more than he lets on, though. Their talk must have worked because, when he came back, he was in a better mood. That was about 20 minutes ago."

"He was fine all afternoon and then he just got all weird on me when he left for the day. I don't know what got into him but he didn't even wait for me and we usually go home together. He's been ignoring my messages all evening yet, now, seems to be my bestie again," I explain.

"I swear men suffer from PMS. James can be insufferable at times, too, but I just feed him and it seems to help," Helen says with a shrug.

"Something must have bothered him and he's taken it out on you. God knows who he was angry texting. You'll have to ask James and let us know," Laura says to Helen.

We turn to the subject of TV as Simon and Harry return with our drinks. They've all been bingeing Line of Duty, ready for the new season coming out this year. I haven't had time to keep up so they try and talk about it in code. I laugh at the explanations they are giving each other, the theories they share and it obviously works because they are following each other and I have no idea what they are talking about.

"You seem in a better mood. You going to tell me what was wrong earlier?" I ask Jake as I stand at the pool table, waiting for my turn. Jake is winning and James is not happy about it.

"We're good, Maggs."

"Because if it was something I did, then you should really tell me."

"It was me, I just - I'm sorry I took it out on you."

I'm not convinced but what can I do if he won't talk to me? "You know, you can talk to me, right? If something is bothering you…" I say but decide to leave it at that when my brother hands me the pool cue.

"You and me, Maggs," Jake says with a wink. "Shall we make this interesting?"

"Depends on what you have in mind."

"The loser has to do karaoke the next time it's on?"

I straighten up. I used to love singing karaoke. Philip and I would always take to the stage at any chance we got, even if we were no good.

"I don't know, Jake."

"What happened to saying yes…?" he trails off as I lean over the table to break.

"Eyes up, Jake," I say striking the cue ball hard and potting three balls. I can't blame him for staring; my date night dress leaves little to the imagination when it comes to cleavage.

"You're trying to distract me."

"Is it working?" I say, nudging him out of the way with my hip to take aim and pot another ball.

"That's not fair," he says his voice a pitch higher. "And it won't work… Loser sings!"

"What isn't fair is that you picked the bet, knowing you have a great singing voice. I, on the other hand, do not."

At least Philip was just as bad as I was at singing so it didn't matter when we both sounded as terrible as each other; we'd laugh all the way through the song anyway.

"You don't do karaoke to sound good, you do it because it's hilarious!"

"A-ha!" I say, triumphant. "So, you *are* doing it because you know I can't sing."

"Maggs, if you wear a dress like that, no one will care that you can't sing… Believe me."

I'm feeling confident when I'm down to my last ball before the black and Jake still has most of his on the table. I take my shot and miss.

Jake stands up straighter and gently chalks his cue. He clears his throat and calmly bends to set up his shot.

Although it's a cold evening, it's warm in the pub. He's wearing a black t-shirt that stretches perfectly over his toned, muscular upper arms and dark jeans that fit him perfectly.

After he pots his first ball, I know I've been hustled. He effortlessly pots each ball, one after the other as I stand there, looking on in disbelief. I really thought I was winning.

He smiles up at me and winks before potting the black ball.

"Asshat."

"Two can play games, Maggs." I'm not going to lie, it felt good seeing him check me out as I bent over the pool table as seductively as I possibly could.

"Maybe I wasn't playing a game," I say suggestively, the alcohol consumption of the evening catching up on me, giving me a false sense of confidence.

"What if I said I liked it?" he says, flirting back. I wonder how far I can push it before its inappropriate but Jake interrupts my thoughts. "Come on, loser. Next round is on me."

We go to the bar and order everyone's drinks and our flirting turns back to our usual banter.

"I've got an idea for you, Maggie. Why don't we set you up on dates?" Harry says to me as we sit down at the table again. He's bouncing in his seat, getting excited which can only mean I am not going to like his suggestion.

"That's a great idea." Laura grins. "I know a lovely man that comes into the bakery every morning who would be perfect for you."

"I am playing no part in this," Jake says, noticeably sliding away from me, his shoulders tense again as he holds his hands up in surrender.

"Why not, Jake? I think it's a great idea," James says, smiling as Jake glares at him.

"His name is Sam," Laura continues. "And he is a children's TV presenter. He's very handsome and such a sweetheart. I think you'll love him."

Jake rolls his eyes when Laura, James, Harry and Simon instantly go into planning mode around me. I barely listen, I'm too busy trying to read Jake who's gone back to sulking in silence.

"Cylvie!" Helen shouts with a wave as I let out a groan. "She's promised to be on her best behaviour," she quietly adds for my benefit now that she knows what a bitch she was to me the other night.

"You know what, I'll take one for the team," Jake says, pushing himself up with two hands on table. He finishes his drink in one and walks away, leaving me baffled for the second time today.

I look at Helen and Laura for support but they both shrug, unable to answer to my unspoken questions. My stomach sinks when he strolls up to Cylvie, turning his charm up to maximum level and puts his arm around her shoulder. She arches her body into his, giggling and I instantly want to stab cocktail sticks in my eyes so I never have to see her again. Obviously, that would be over dramatic so, instead, I go for a childish reaction which is to pick up my bag, finish my drink before slamming my glass on the table and going home, alone.

Unfortunately for me, Cylvie gets the last unspoken word in when she runs her bony fingers up Jake's bicep, wrapping her long arms around his neck as he tightens his hold on her tiny waist. The piece de resistance is when she leans into his ear to whisper something to him and winks right at me. She thinks she's won a game I wasn't really playing to begin with.

Suddenly, I feel drained, I don't have the energy to wonder why I care so much about Jake and Cylvie. All I want is to do is to curl up in my comfiest pyjamas, order a takeaway and find something binge worthy to watch on Netflix.

***

After the shitty night I'd had on my date and Jake's ever-changing mood swings giving me whiplash, all I wanted to do was hide under my warm duvet. I wanted to sleep all day in the hope that, when I woke up, everything would have been a really, really, bad dream.

Alas, it was not. It was very much real life.

The awful date, Cylvie draping her unfairly gorgeous self around Jake and the thoughts of what probably happened after I left fill my brain, causing me to smother my face in my pillow. Not like I have the right to an opinion on the matter. He's a single, consenting man and he can shag whoever he wants.

Just... why does it have to be her? And why do I care?

It's probably because I can't bear to see Cylvie's face in the pub every Friday night and I don't want her hanging around my office all the time if they start dating. That's it.

I groan as my phone vibrates for the ten millionth time this morning. Maybe, if I pull the covers back over my head, I can go back to sleep and continue ignoring people. I used to be so good at that.

I had almost started dreaming again when I am pulled from my unconsciousness once more. This time, it was to the sound of my doorbell buzzing. I groan and make my way through the living room as I huff and puff in annoyance to answer the door to my unwelcome visitor. I pause to pick up my phone on the way from the breakfast bar.

Twelve missed calls from Jake, probably wondering why I didn't stick around last night to see him paw all over the spawn of Satan.

"Hello," I answer the buzzer that opens the outside door to my flat.

"Did you forget?" Jake asks me.

"What?"

"Buzz me in."

I pause for a second before pressing the button that opens the main door and leave the door to my flat open so he can let himself in.

I bought this flat a year after Philip died. Before then, we had been living with my parents while we looked for a home of our own that we never got around to buying. After the accident, I needed help for a little while but found that I wasn't getting the independence I needed to heal when I had Mum looking after me, helping me walk, feeding me and doing my washing. It's only a small, one bedroom flat with an open plan kitchen/living space and a small bathroom off the bedroom but it's enough for me. It's homely and it's obvious a woman lives here alone. Candles on every available surface, photographs on the walls, cushions and blankets pretty much everywhere and a fridge filled with more wine bottles and chocolate than actual food.

"You forgot," he says as he shuts the door behind him, looking at me in my pyjamas and unbrushed bed hair. "Unless you want to go outside wearing Hufflepuff pyjamas? I would have thought you would identify more as a Ravenclaw since you're so clever."

I ignore his knowledge of Hogwarts houses and his poor attempt at flattery. Instead, I turn back to make my way to the kitchen. He follows me as I turn on my coffee machine.

"I didn't forget I just… I figured you'd be busy. With *Cylvie*. Coffee?" I ask, holding up a mug and hoping I didn't sound as harsh in real life as it sounded in my head.

"Are you kidding?" he says, turning me to face him. "She's awful to you every time she's around and you'd already had a rough night. I figured that I'd have the best chance of distracting her and keeping her away from you given the fact she's tried to get in my pants for the better part of 10 years."

"So, to get her off my back, you put her on hers?" I snap. God, why am I so mad about this? They're grown, consenting adults and it's really none of my business.

I turn again to make us a coffee. He didn't say that he wanted one but I know him well enough to know he won't turn it down.

"For Christ sake, I didn't shag Cylvie," he almost shouts at me.

"What?" I ask, unable to look at him.

"I didn't have sex with Cylvie," he says, turning me around to face him again. This time, he doesn't let go so I'm forced to look at him. "I took her to get a drink to keep her away from you then I saw you storm out so I ditched her at the bar with Helen and went home. Alone. I tried to ring you last night to see if I could come and talk to you but you didn't answer."

Well, shit. That brings me back down to earth with a bump.

"So, now that we have that cleared up, can you go and get dressed? We've got plans."

I do as I'm told, feeling terribly embarrassed and a little guilty for thinking the worst.

I quickly shower, get dressed and put on my make-up while Jake lounges on my bed, idly watching TV.

"Man, I have got to get me one of these beds," he says,

admiring the fact the TV rises out of the foot of the bed. When I told him about it, he was like a kid at Christmas, inspecting every inch of it before making himself incredibly comfortable on my side.

"Are you going to tell me why you we're so upset at the thought of Cylvie and me together?" he asks, watching me in my dressing table mirror as I brush my freshly blow-dried hair.

"No. It's stupid"

"I'm not disputing that... I'm 99.9% sure it's stupid," he says, taunting me.

"I'll tell you if you tell me who you were angry texting last night at the pub, Helen and Laura told me."

He sighs as he combs his fingers through his hair, probably weighing up whether or not telling me is worth opening up. It's the only way I can think of avoiding the subject of Cylvie because, I'll be honest, I really don't know why I'm so against her. Yeah, she is mean and cruel but, deep down, I want her approval, I *want* her to like me. I've always been the type of person who needs validation, the type of person that needs to be liked by everyone. As far as I'm aware, I've done nothing to offend her and, yet, she constantly cuts me down. It grates on me.

Yeah, like I said, stupid.

"I was texting you," he finally says. I really didn't expect this conversation to continue so I turn on my stool to face him.

"Me? Why?" I say, taken by surprise.

"The whole you-on-a-date thing took me off guard.

You're my friend, Maggs, and I know we haven't had a great relationship for a few years but you're still one of my oldest and best friends and you didn't tell me you were dating again. I care about you. I want you to be safe. I know that the decision to start dating must have been a hard one to make. I just want you to know that you can talk to me about anything and, since we've spent every recent waking moment either together or talking to each other, I didn't expect you to keep that a secret from me. I don't know what else to say other than 'I'm sorry'."

"Oh," is all I can muster in response to him.

I turn back to face my dressing table mirror and busy myself with my mascara while I digest what he's said.

"She's not good enough for you," I say, grabbing his attention again and meeting his eyes in mirror. "She is mean and narcissistic and you deserve better. You deserve someone who is honest and kind and brings out the best in you."

"I don't know about that. I've not been the best behaved myself when it comes to women."

"Everyone makes mistakes, we've all done things we're not proud of. You should focus on the person you are now, not the person you once were, because the Jake you are now deserves the world."

"Is that what you're doing? Focusing on who you are now?"

"I'm trying to. It would help if I knew who I was anymore," I admit. "I'm still figuring that part out."

***

After our honest talk in my flat, Jake and I spend the day slowly wandering around Borough Market, all tensions left behind. He links my arm through his as we peruse the different stalls, aimlessly trying to narrow down what we want to eat for lunch. There is just far too much choice.

The smell of delicious world food fills the air and, with every moment that passes, my stomach growls louder and louder in protest. I never did order that take away last night, settling for a packet of chocolate Hobnobs and a Cherry Bakewell, instead.

Okay, three Cherry Bakewells but I'd had a bad night so I was comfort eating.

"Can you just pick something, please?" Jake begs me. "You're making some strange noises over there."

"Okay... Paella," I say, eventually making up my mind.

"I don't like seafood," he moans.

"You can get something else, you know? We don't have to eat the same thing," I argue.

"But, if I get something you like, you'll want some which isn't fair on me, is it?" he whines on. "You know I can't say no to you when you want feeding."

I laugh because it's true. I often get FOMO when it comes to food and he always shares with me even when he doesn't want to.

"Has anyone ever told you that you act like a toddler when you're hungry?" I say. He looks at me with the cutest pet lip and I can't stop the laughter bubbling up again.

"Okay, fine, you decide. What do *you* want to eat?" I ask, slowly like I'm talking to a child.

"I feel like pizza," he eventually says.

"Okay, you get pizza and I'll get a spag bol and we can split them."

He agrees so I quickly take his hand and lead him back through the crowd to the Italian stall we walked past about an hour ago.

"I feel like I need to remind you that I'm lactose intolerant so we will either have to pick vegan cheese or go cheeseless."

"I know, Jake, I remember."

We pick up our food and walk towards the river to a secluded bench in Sarah Ballantyne Square. Although it's a bit cold and gloomy, the rain and wind thankfully hold off.

"This was the best idea you've had today," he says, taking a bite of our cheese-less pizza.

"I have those, occasionally."

My phone noisily vibrates for the umpteenth time today.

"What is going on with your phone?" Jake asks.

I just groan as I look at the screen. Yet more dick pics. Great.

He takes my phone off me and his face drops when he notices what it is.

"Okay, I am taking you off this bloody app. How many of those have you gotten?" he says, holding it up to my face to unlock it.

"Please do. I lost count at thirty-five or something."

He looks horrified and, after a few minutes of silently seething to himself, he hands my phone back.

"There, your profiles are deleted and apps are uninstalled."

"Thanks. It should have been the first thing I did when I got home last night," I say, putting my phone away again and returning to our food.

***

After we polished off the very last bite of our delicious lunch, we went back to the market to pick up some produce and then went in search of a pub. I was parched after a day of walking around the busy market and our arms ached after being loaded down with bags of amazing food.

I couldn't leave without stocking up on the freshest fruit I've ever seen: It makes the fruit in the supermarket look like scraps. Not to mention the enormous cakes we passed on our way out that I had to buy! Jake insisted on buying burgers to make for our dinner tonight so we picked the plumpest tomatoes and the best potatoes we could find at the greengrocers along with some deliciously smelling, fresh bread buns to complete our meal.

We hid away in the warm, cosy pub for hours until we decided we were almost too drunk to cook and had better make our way back to Jake's flat.

I had never been in Jake's flat before tonight and it's surprising how neat and tidy it is for a bachelor pad, especially considering the chaos his side of our office is in. He has bookshelves full of DVDs, CDs and all of the old vinyl records he's collected over the years. When I question if he has a need for CDs *and* DVD's (since he already has subscriptions to 4 different TV and movie streaming platforms plus Amazon Music) his answer is simple.

"What if the Internet went down?" he proposes. I can't fault his logic.

I pull out a CD and smile as the memories hit me. "You still have this CD?"

"Uh, yes, it's amazing!"

I mess about with his CD player, select track two and the Fratellis' 'Chelsea Dagger' plays on the surround sound. The music takes me back to a time where we had no worries and trauma didn't haunt me on a daily basis.

"I used to love this song," I say, grinning. "You would always have it playing in your car when you would pick us up from school after you had finished sixth form. Everyone thought you we're so cool because you listened to Indie Rock, wore a leather jacket and drove an old, shitty Citroen Saxo."

"Good because I thought I was so cool."

"The girls in my year would go crazy wanting to wait with me, Philip and Laura so they could catch a small glimpse of you."

"Teenage girls are apparently easy to please if all it took was me turning up in my shitty car."

"Every girl in our school fancied you and James. It was all I heard about for years; horny teenage girls talking about what they wanted to do to my brother and best friend." I pretend to wretch at the thought.

He laughs because he knows it's true. He knew that, back then, everyone fancied him and he loved it.

"You know, you were pretty cool, too. The way you'd immediately jump up and dance whenever the Arctic Monkeys would come on the radio. You'd wear your short skirts, even in the winter, and those white sand shoes you'd get from the army surplus shop in town. You always looked way better than the girls who'd walk around with a face full of cheap make-up and fake designer clothes and handbags they'd buy in Benidorm on their summer holidays."

His compliment makes me smile. I don't tell him how much I envied those girls growing up, how I still envy girls like that. Like Cylvie. Except, with her, the fake stuff is most definitely designer fresh from Milan, Paris or New York and her make-up is expertly applied by the best make-up artists in the country.

I had forgotten all about those shoes until he brought it up. They were the most comfortable shoes I'd ever owned and I insisted on wearing them everywhere. My style hasn't changed that much. Even now, when I am not working, I opt for skinny jeans and my worn-out Adidas Gazelles. I wear high heels and expensive dresses for work but it's the last thing I want to wear on a weekend.

Jake connects his phone to the speakers and searches for a suitable playlist while I open the bottle of red wine we bought at one of the stalls today. We get started on cooking our burgers as we sing along and dance in the kitchen to late noughties Indie Rock anthems. It's surprising how many of the words we remember considering I haven't listened to this music in years. Jake appoints me sous chef and I happily help by chopping the potatoes into chips, ready to go in the air fryer.

"For a man who eats out a lot, you have all the kitchen gadgets, don't you?" I say, looking around his kitchen at the various appliances.

"I love cooking, I just don't have the time to do it very often. Mum taught me how to cook and bake so I used to help her all the time when we were growing up. Dad would go off to the football on a weekend and I preferred to stay home and bake a cake or pie or whatever else with Mum."

"I always remember you being a mummy's boy. It's really sweet."

"I always have been a mummy's boy. I'm not ashamed to admit it," he says, smiling.

"I loved spending time with my dad and I always wanted to be just like him but I was a mummy's girl. She's my best friend… Or she was, at least. I just wish I had time to go out there more often than I do."

"My mum misses you, too, you know? She talks about you all the time. Every time she calls me, you're at the top of her list of questions. You and Laura are like daughters to her."

I think about that for a second. I really should make the effort and spend more time with Mum and Jake's Mum, Margaret, as well as Laura's mum, Angie. I make a mental note to plan a girl's day sometime soon, maybe to the theatre. We always said we'd go see Mamma Mia but never got around to it. I get excited thinking about how much fun we used to have on our nights out and quickly text Laura my plan to search online for tickets in the morning.

I know it'll make our mums happy but, not only that, it'll make me happy, too.

CHAPTER SEVEN

Laura: Let us know when you're home safe. Enjoy your date!

Helen: And tell us all about it!

Maggie: There's not much to tell. He's half an hour late. I'm leaving in 5 when I've finished my wine. Are you at the pub?

"This dating thing is turning out to be one big failure after another. Last week, I end up in handcuffs - Not the kinky kind, the police kind - because they thought I was involved in my Tinder date's drug cartel or whatever. This week, my date stands me up," I say to the waitress as I pay for my wine. "Oh god-," I say, suddenly distracted by what I see - or rather, who.

"Is that your date?" she asks, staring at Jake as he makes his way to my table.

"No, he's my business partner and my best friend. We're close enough for this to be really embarrassing for me."

He smiles at the waitress as she leaves my table with a reassuring pat on my shoulder.

Christ. Kill me, now.

"Jake! What are you doing here?" I ask, trying not to think about how gorgeous he looks in the dim candlelight of the restaurant.

After our day at Borough Market last Saturday, we spent the rest of the night in his flat. We had far too much to drink and I fell asleep on his couch. When I woke up in his bed the next morning, I feared the worst, worried that I had done something I couldn't take back. Turns out we had both passed out on the sofa and, when he woke up a few hours later, he carried me to his bed and he took himself back to the sofa like a gentleman.

Earlier in the week (as promised), Laura had set me up with the guy that goes into her bakery. This time, I took no chances and told Jake right away. Instead of reacting the way he did last time, he was okay about it all. That being said, he didn't seem too interested in knowing more than the date and venue so we didn't talk about it all week.

"I'm meeting my team for our belated Christmas night out at Junkyard Golf and this is the only Friday that everyone could get together. It's just down the road and I saw you through the window. Thought I'd say hi and check how your date is going, see if I needed to intimidate anyone."

Right, he did tell me about that. I should have known he'd walk right past here before I chose the window seat. Now would be an appropriate time for the ground to open and swallow me up.

"You haven't checked the group chat then?" I say as I finish my glass of wine and stand to put my coat on.

"No, what's up?" he says, getting his phone out to catch up on the messages he's missed. "Oh," he adds as he reads.

"I don't want to keep you. I'm just going to go home and wallow in my own self-pity," I say with an exasperated sigh. "Might swing by The George to see the others."

"Come with me! Brian had childcare issues and had to cancel but we already booked his spot and it's paid for."

"I shouldn't. I don't want to intrude."

"You can't waste a gorgeous dress like that by going home at 8 o'clock. Please?" he asks nicely as he wraps my scarf around me, carefully un-tucking my hair from the back. "I'm not going to take 'no' for an answer so you can spare us the argument and just come with me?"

I beam up at him. "I have been wanting to go there for ages."

"Besides that, I need you to keep me on the straight and narrow. In the office, my team are professional, hardworking individuals. After a couple of drinks, they're like wild animals and you know how easily lead I am."

He offers me his arm the way he always does and we step into the frosty winter air which sparks an involuntary shudder up my spine.

"Are you cold?" he asks as I pull my coat tighter around my body.

"Yeah, but I'll warm up when we start walking."

He takes off his thick, wool scarf and wraps it around my

shoulders.

"Aren't *you* cold now?"

"I've just spent half an hour on a hot, sweaty tube. I need to cool down," he says, smiling as he links my arm back through his.

It's amazing how comfortable this has become, Jake and I walking closely together with either my arm linking his or his arm around my shoulder.

"Are you sure your team won't mind me tagging along?" I ask nervously. "Should you not call someone and double check?"

"Of course not. Anyway, you know most of them now that they've moved up with us," he says in an attempt to reassure me.

It's only a short walk from the restaurant to Junkyard Golf and, as we turn off the main road onto a pedestrian street, the bar is hard to miss. Neon flashing lights and the thumping base of the music coming from the small, windowed entryway announce its location.

Since we're last to arrive, almost everyone is already waiting inside.

"You're late," a girl I don't recognise says with a smile.

"I had to pick up a straggler," Jake answers, patting my arm as I smile at the girl.

"Hi, I'm Claire," the girl says, holding out her hand with a welcoming smile.

"Maggie."

"I know who you are and it's lovely to finally meet you.

I've heard so many wonderful things," she says, winking at Jake who just rolls his eyes at her.

"Claire is currently on maternity leave. She comes back next month - Thank God. She's the best Copy Writer we have and we miss her dearly."

"Everyone else is inside, come on," she says, leading the way through the doors to the most brilliantly chaotic place I've ever set foot in.

It's like I'm walking into the Tardis. The small entryway leads way to a much bigger bar area surrounded by chain link fence, exposed brickwork and much more neon. Even the golf balls are fluorescent. A dozen familiar faces greet us with enthusiasm. I make my way around the group and, by the time I'm finished saying hello to everyone, Claire is back from the bar with two huge cocktails decorated with party rings and popping candy.

"There are 7 cocktails and 2 alcoholic slushes on the menu. I say we try them all. This one is called 'Hotline Ting'," she says grinning at me as I eagerly take the pink and purple drink from her. "I don't get out often so I'm making the most of a child-free night," she explains as she takes a large mouthful of the colourful liquid.

"Cheers to that," I say as we clink glasses.

"So, how long have you and Jake been together?"

"Oh, we're not..."

"Sorry, I just assumed... You looked so comfortable with each other, that's all. Pretend I didn't say anything," she says, waving her hand in dismissal.

"We've just known each other a really long time," I answer with a smile.

"I always thought he had a thing for you. He would make the most ridiculous excuses to see you in person even though an email would suffice. Maybe he just wanted to skive," she shrugs, echoing what Jude had said when I met him in the office.

Before I can react, Jake comes and tells us it's time to start so we drop our coats off at the cloak room and make our way to our course. We're split into 4 teams and I'm relieved when Jake tells me I'm paired with him, Claire and Jude. We head towards the course called 'Gary' which is themed around a car scrapyard. Obstacles include: a huge tyre, a grown-up sized slide and a bunch of written-off cars. The amount of detail put into this place is incredible; you can see why it gets amazing reviews.

"Don't worry, I'll go easy on you," Jake says with a wink.

"You don't remember last time we played crazy golf, do you?"

"Oh, man. I forgot all about that. I haven't thought about that day in a long time. For a bloke that was perfect at everything, Philip was so shit when it came to crazy golf," he says, laughing fondly at the memory.

"Yeah, that's why we got banned from that place in Kingston," I say, laughing as I think back to the time he went to putt the ball just inches from the hole but, instead, hit it so hard it smashed the windmill two holes over. We were asked to never return after that day which was, coincidentally, the last time I played. "They never replaced that windmill blade, you know? I noticed when I drove passed it at New Year's."

"No way! I remember that you won that game. I should probably be worried."

"Don't worry, I'll go easy on you," I say, echoing his earlier statement.

"I suppose you do owe me a thrashing since I hustled you at pool."

I huff at him and pretend to be annoyed but I can't keep it up for more than a few seconds before I burst out laughing. "I should have worn a more revealing dress," I say, looking down at my suitably-covered cleavage.

"You'll have to remember next time."

Claire decides to go first and Jude, second. Apparently, they are just as competitive as we are so they are too busy trash talking one another to hear our exchange.

"You and James went off to uni the next day," I say after a few moments of silence.

"I remember." He doesn't have to tell me what he's thinking because I know it's the same as me: It's the last time we hung out as a group. I remember the day vividly. I thought about it a lot when they were gone. Did we do something to make him retreat? Was it something I said? Or Philip or Laura? Or was I wrong in thinking we were friends in the first place? I never did get the answers to those questions but I tell myself that it doesn't matter. Look at us now! We're closer than ever before but, deep down, I know those questions still plague me.

***

I can't believe I forgot how much fun Crazy Golf is. Maybe it's the added alcohol, the fabulous company and the cool atmosphere but I've had such a wonderful night. Claire and I made it to 5 cocktails before she drunkenly declared she'd had enough which I was glad about because I don't know how I'd cope with another hangover.

Tomorrow evening, Laura and I are taking the mums to dinner before we go to the theatre to see Mamma Mia. We even invited Jake's mum. How will I explain to Margaret that it's her son's fault I'm hungover without anyone jumping to conclusions? They already think we're hiding some sort of sordid affair from them.

Of course, even after fourteen years, I am still the reigning champion of crazy golf which pleases me, no end. Jake was a gracious loser despite his threats to bring me back once he's had enough practice to beat me. Our competitive streaks really shone as the night went on, both of us trying our absolute best to win. Claire and Jude gave up halfway around the course and decided to reverse the rules, battling it out between the two of them over who could get the highest number of points.

"Tell me again why you and Jake aren't together," Claire had said to me halfway through the game as I stood back, admiring

Jake as he putts.

"I think you need your eyes testing," I say with a laugh. "There is nothing going on between us, just friendly competition."

"Okay, you can keep telling me that but I know sexual tension when I see it. Babe, you're flirting with him just as hard as he is with you."

Her words echo in my mind for the rest of the evening. I admit, we flirt a lot more than we used too but that's just the kind of friendship we have. It doesn't mean anything, just like it didn't mean anything when he turned up at the restaurant and insisted that I join him tonight. He was just being friendly.

"I don't think I've seen you smile so much as you have tonight," Jake says, playfully nudging me as we walk to the tube station. Clearly, he didn't learn from last time he playfully nudged me. He knows I have terrible balance and, of course, I go spinning out again. This time, he pulls me by my waist to catch me and I fall into him, landing flush against his chest. Thankfully, he remains unmoved and I manage to find my balance but I don't release the hold I have on his shoulders. The sudden contact of his strong hold on my waist and the feel of his solid muscle beneath my hands has taken my breath away and has my pulse racing.

"You should try to be more careful," he says, a smile pulling at the corners of his mouth. I, on the other hand, have no words. Yes, he's dazzled me many times before with his good looks and kind personality but this is much more than being dazzled.

There is an invisible force pulling us together, closing the distance between us as we stand in the empty street.

He keeps his arms tightly around me, holding me close to him as his beautiful, blue eyes bore into mine. All signs of joking and banter have disappeared, replaced by something I can't quite put my finger on. My heart is pounding so fast that I can hear it in my ears and the butterflies that have taken up residence in my stomach are going nuts. His face is mere inches from mine and I know that, if I just stood on my tiptoes, I could easily kiss him.

I want to kiss him.

The realisation hits me hard. What am I doing?! Obviously, I don't want to kiss him. It's Jake. My friend, Jake. My business partner, Jake.

So why can't I look away?

Because it's Jake and I don't want to.

"Well..." I say as he leans his face towards mine, his full lips parted slightly. The small movement is enough for me to come to my senses and move back slightly so I can try to regain some composure. "Thanks for catching me, even though you pushed me but whatever." I aim for joking but struggle to make my voice sound anything other than desperately turned on.

"I'll have to remember your distinct lack of balancing skills next time," he says, straightening up and clearing his throat.

We continue our walk to the tube in silence. It's not an awkward silence, it's comfortable. This time, we don't link arms. Instead, he has his hands stuffed in his pockets as though he's willing them to stay there. The entire time we're walking side by side, I'm thinking about that almost kiss and the fact I *definitely* wanted him to kiss me. I can't make sense of it all. Maybe it's Claire? She got in my head with everything she said. Maybe it was the alcohol making me see things that aren't there?

I risk a look at Jake. He doesn't see me glance at him but, as I do, my heart suddenly races again and I feel nervous. It's as though, all this time, these feelings have been there but, now, they're in the forefront of my mind and are begging to be addressed.

***

"Do you want to talk about what happened earlier? With your date, I mean," he asks, breaking our silence when we reach the door to my flat.

Do I want to talk about my date standing me up?

No.

Do I want to talk about our almost kiss?

Again, no.

Do I want him to try and kiss me again?

Yes, very much so, but, at the same time, no.

I don't want to leave with a huge question mark hanging over us but I don't know what to say.

"I opened a bottle of wine earlier. I only had one glass. You can come in and help me finish it, if you want?"

Yeah, I know how it sounds.

"Lead the way." He follows me into the building and up the first flight of stairs to my little flat.

I pour the wine from the open bottle in the fridge and hand him his glass.

He was lying in my bed the other morning and I didn't feel nervous at all but, standing here, in my kitchen, my heart might explode with anticipation. Clearly, my body doesn't get the hint that Jake and I are just friends and is reacting to him in ways it really shouldn't.

"I bought you something," he says as he opens his backpack, pulling something soft out and handing it to me.

I open the T-shirt and let out a laugh when I see what it is. It's a T-shirt from Junkyard Golf that reads 'Do you even golf, bro?'.

"I love it! Thank you," I say, standing on my tip toes to hug him, wrapping my arms around his neck.

"I got one too so we can match. Mine says 'Gals that golf'. I thought you'd get a kick out of it." I laugh again as he holds it up to show me.

"I'll be right back; I'm going to put mine on. Put yours on, too," I say, skipping to my bedroom.

I quickly comb through my wavy hair with my fingers and spray a little deodorant when I change out of my date night dress.

I try to get my head around what happened earlier but I can't seem to shake this feeling of confusion. I'm sure Jake was about to kiss me. Wasn't he? Why did I move away when he leaned in? Do I want him to try again? I'm not sure I should answer myself honestly.

I pull myself together and join him again on the couch in my new T-shirt, black leggings and bright pink slipper socks. He's put his new T-shirt on, too, and my heart swells. He reaches his arm out and pulls me into his side, passing me my drink.

"We need a selfie in our t-shirts. Jude will go nuts over it for his Insta campaign." He pulls out his phone and takes the photo. "Beautiful," he says as he shows me the photo.

It's a simple photo, the two of us in our matching t-shirts and smiling straight at the camera. He swipes along to show me another which looks as though I thought he was done taking photos because I'm no longer looking at the camera. Instead, I'm looking right up at Jake with the biggest grin on my face.

Jude pitched us his idea for our social media earlier in the week and it was a great pitch. We got him on the job right away and already we've got over 20,000 followers. Some of the posts are about us and what we do day-to-day, some are general titbits about the company. Earlier today, Jude said he was going to post some of us playing golf so he could try and create a more relatable vibe to the profile. He ended up getting a free round of drinks from the bar because he told them he would tag them in the photos as free publicity.

We sit in a comfortable silence for a few minutes while he sends the photo to Jude before he speaks again.

"I don't want you to think I'm creepy or anything but I did take some photos of you tonight. I think you should see them." I narrow my eyes in suspicion as he pulls more photos up to show me. "Maggs, you look so happy here. You've had the most amazingly goofy grin all night and it made me happy to see it again. I know you're still working out the kind of person you want to be but you just need to look here to see that you're the same hilarious sixteen-year-old I knew and loved."

He swipes through the photos of me lining up my shot, celebrating when I got a hole in one on an impossible course and dancing with Claire and Jude to the 90's rave tunes that blasted through the neon-soaked room.

"I felt it too," I say honestly. "Every day, I feel more and more alive. Like I'm coming back to life, almost. Maybe that's a morbid way of looking at it but, tonight, I felt free from everything and it felt great. I want to be like that more often; it felt really good."

I swipe through the rest of his photos: Selfies of the four of us, selfies of just the two us, photos of Claire and Jude messing with the props and photos of Jake and I just having a wonderful time together.

"For what it's worth, Maggs, that bloke missed out tonight but his loss was my gain." His comment takes me off guard. "I mean it, you look incredible and you're funny and everyone loved having you there tonight. I loved having you there tonight," he says as I lean in to rest my head against his chest. His hand starts drawing shapes on my arm.

"Maybe I should just give up dating. I'm obviously not good at it"

"You've got so much love to give. You just need to find the right man to go on a date with."

Like Jake Mills maybe?

I give my head a metaphorical shake.

Whatever happened earlier was just an anomaly. Jake doesn't kiss anyone who he can't ditch the next day and he can't ditch me when we work in the same office.

But he did buy us matching t-shirts.

My ringing phone breaks our silence.

"Hey, it's Sam," says the voice as I answer. I'm thankful for the distraction. "I'm so sorry I stood you up tonight."

"Okay...?" I say, unsure of why he is calling me at this time of night after missing our date. Is this a booty call?

"It was shitty and I'm really sorry but I have a really good excuse, if you'll hear me out?"

"Go ahead," I say in my most non-committal tone, as if I'm only humouring him.

"I play football on a Friday afternoon; I had a bad tackle and I broke my collarbone. I've only just got home from A&E." That quickly snaps me out of my mood.

"Oh, my god. Are you okay?" That is one hell of a painful excuse.

"Yeah, there's nothing you can do for a broken collarbone

except stick it in a sling and take some painkillers. Except...
Maybe beg for a second chance with a beautiful woman? What do
you say?"

Jake raises his eyebrows at me quizzically.

"Since you've made such a solid case, how does Monday
night sound?" I say to Sam.

"Thank God, I thought I'd blown it," he says with a
relieved laugh. "Monday is perfect. I'll pick you up at 7? Text me
your address."

We say our goodbyes, I wish Sam happy healing and we
hang up.

"That was Sam, my date that stood me up. He's been in
the hospital. He broke his collarbone this afternoon."

"Right, he couldn't text you and tell you this earlier instead
of leaving you alone at that restaurant?"

"I'm sure that, after breaking his collarbone, he had other
things on his mind."

"Okay," Jake says as he puts his drink down on the coffee
table. "I should be getting home, it's late."

"What's the problem? It's a valid excuse." I can feel it
happening again. We're about to argue and I can't stop it.

"I'm just saying, he could have texted you instead of
ditching you like that. It's a bit of a dick move. You're worth more
than that."

"Well, it's not your decision whether or not I give him a
second chance, it's mine."

"No, you're right," he says as he pulls his coat on.

"Why are you leaving? Don't leave."

"It's late and it's been a long day so I'm just going to go home." He kisses me on the cheek for the first time and his soft lips gently brush my skin. I want to lean into him, to feel him. I want him to give me more than just a peck on the cheek. I want him to give me a reason not to go on that date. "Have a good time at the theatre tomorrow."

"If you have something to say to me, just say it," I say, barely above a whisper.

"It's not the right time, Maggs. The moment has gone. I'm sorry."

The happy mood I felt a little over five minutes ago dissolves as he closes the door behind him.

It's probably for the best that we didn't continue the conversation. One of us would have yelled (more than likely, me) and we would both feel terrible in the morning. What would the alternative be? We kiss and live happily ever after? No way, it doesn't work like that.

I should be relieved that he left before I could ruin everything but I'm not. Instead, I'm barely holding back tears as I take our glasses to the kitchen and pour the wine down the sink.

Something catches my eye, sticking out of my bag as I walk towards my bedroom. It's the strip of photos we got from the photo booth in the bar. My heart aches when I think about the fun we had together tonight, how much we'd laughed at the different filters in the booth and pulled funny faces at the camera. I think about how I ruined it all by answering that call.

I take the thin strip to my bedroom and wedge it into the mirror frame on my dressing table. Then, I crawl into bed, alone, sad and wearing my new t-shirt.

What a terrible end to a wonderful evening.

CHAPTER EIGHT

When I woke up this morning, I was hungover and exhausted from a night of tossing and turning, unable to get comfortable. Although I was tired, I just couldn't switch my brain off. I kept re-playing the events of the evening, wishing I had said something else to Jake, made different choices. I try to make sense of it all but, the more I try to figure it all out, the less I can understand.

I think about the fun we had playing crazy golf, the almost 'moment' we had in the street and the feelings it has stirred up from somewhere deep inside of me. I think of my amazing T-shirt (which is now my new favourite thing to sleep in), I see the pictures he took of me when I didn't notice and how happy I looked in them. Then, I think about Jake leaving my flat in a completely different mood than when he entered it. I hated seeing the look he gave me as he left.

I should ring him and apologise but I have no idea what I would be apologising for. I want to speak to him but I don't know what I'd say.

"So, he just left?" Laura asks once I've finished telling her about my night. "No explanation?"

When I called her and told her to meet me at the West End restaurant early to examine everything in detail, she agreed right away. I was hoping she could make some sense out of it all from an outside perspective.

"Yeah, it was weird. He made up a stupid excuse that it was late and practically ran out of the door. Usually, he texts me during the day or he'll send me random pictures of things he thinks I'll like but it's, what, 5 pm? I've not heard from him at all today. I almost feel like I should apologise to him but I don't know why. It's not like I did anything wrong."

"Well, you did agree to go on a date with another man in front of him... Less than an hour after he almost kissed you."

"It's Jake. He kisses a lot of people he doesn't mean to."

"If you ask me - which you did - I think he wanted to kiss you then you pulled away, making him second guess himself. He would have tried again if you hadn't answered the phone to Sam but then, when you arranged another date, with a man that wasn't him... He realised he'd missed his window. That's why he left in a hurry. His ego was hurt and he's probably a little embarrassed," Laura says, stressing each sentence by prodding the table between us with her index finger.

'The moment has gone,' that's what he'd said to me.

"That would make sense if he wanted to kiss me. I've gone through it in my mind so many times that now I'm not so sure he did try to kiss me. Maybe I made it up in my mind."

"Come on, Maggie. He obviously fancies you, we can all

tell. He sits with you at any opportunity, he flirts with you like crazy and he always has his arm around you. Whenever he looks at you, he gets these big, loving eyes that I've honestly never seen on him, like, ever."

"He flirts with everyone."

"Does he though? Because he doesn't flirt with me or Helen. He doesn't look at us like he looks at you."

Come to think of it, I haven't seen him flirt with anyone recently and I haven't seen him hook up either.

"Have you seen the photos on Instagram?" Laura asks me, pulling out her phone.

"I don't have an account."

"Firstly, you need to sign up and then look at your own company profile. You might even see something you like."

"I will when I get home. Give me yours," I say, taking the phone off her.

I bring up our profile and (like Jude promised) there is a new story. The first picture is of me and Jake standing proudly with our golf clubs.

'Our very own Commanders-in-Chief went head-to-head tonight. Stay tuned to find out who wins!'

There are other random photos of everyone having a fantastic time, smiling and laughing while posing on the various courses. I laugh as I watch the videos back, explaining to Laura who the different people are.

There are videos of me, too, drinking cocktails with

Claire, attempting to coach Jude into making better shots. I keep scrolling through until I see, right there, on the screen, me and Jake looking extremely comfortable with each other. I'm celebrating my win and, when he comes over to throw me over his shoulder, I squeal and laugh without a care in the world.

I remember how I felt in that moment and it's a far cry from how I feel now.

Before we can continue our conversation, our mums walk into the restaurant so we quickly pretend to talk about something else. In the back of my mind, all I'm thinking about is what Laura has said. I haven't really thought about how Jake looks at me but I do know how I feel when his eyes meet mine, how my stomach feels like it's doing somersaults and my heart speeds up ever so slightly.

So, what if we flirt a lot and sit by each other a lot or if he reminds me of a time when life was much simpler?

As our Mums get to our table, we share kisses and excited hellos so I try to put all thoughts of him to the side. We've all been looking forward to tonight and overthinking things isn't going to ruin it for me.

"It's been so long since we've done this," Mum says as she takes her seat next to me and squeezes my hand. "Thank you for arranging everything, I can't wait to see the show."

"You should be thanking Helen, she managed to get us great seats," I say.

"It's the sing-along show, too," Laura says excitedly. "We

can sing along to our hearts content without being shushed."

"Sweetheart, there's nothing nice about the five of us singing," Angie, Laura's mum, says with a laugh. "Is Helen performing tonight?"

"Yes, she's playing one of Sophie's friends," Laura answers. "She said she will meet us for a drink afterwards."

"What are we drinking, ladies? Red, white, pink?" Jake's mum, Margaret, asks.

It's a unanimous vote for rosé so she orders two bottles from the waiter and my plan of an evening on Diet Coke went out the window. The waiter comes over to deliver our order and we all sit and chat. It reminds me of old times when we would do this more often.

Two hours pass quickly when everyone is enjoying themselves and its eventually time to make our way to the theatre.

"So, how are you finding working with my Jake?" Margaret asks me as she walks with me and Laura while Mum and Angie trail along behind.

"It's going really well, working with him is great," I say as Laura gives me a knowing smile.

"And he's been hanging around with us quite a lot, too," Laura chips in. "It's good to have him back."

"I'm glad. It'll keep him out of trouble. I never did like the kind of company he has been known to keep," his mum says, pausing to think for a moment. "I only ask because- Well... he's been rather..."

"Moody? Sensitive? A pain in the arse?" Laura replies with suggested adjectives.

"Exactly."

"We've noticed that, too," I say. "I'll talk to him on Monday see if he'll tell me what's going on."

"I think he might have a secret girlfriend," his mum says.

I can't explain why my stomach feels like it's dragging on the ground while simultaneously getting stuck in my throat but the thought of him secretly seeing someone is unnerving. None of this makes sense. Why would he try to kiss me if he were already seeing someone?

"He hasn't said anything but we'll look out for him, don't worry," Laura says as I struggle to use my words.

Mum and Angie finally catch up and the subject changes to what we should drink here which provides welcome relief from hearing about Jake's potential girlfriend.

"You go ahead and get our seats, we'll bring the drinks," Laura says, dragging me to the bar.

Mum gives me a funny look as though she's trying to read my emotions but failing.

"Still telling yourself you don't have feelings for him?" Laura says in a hushed tone.

Is that what this feeling is? Yeah, he's good looking, he's charming and chivalrous. He makes me laugh and I love spending time with him.

"Oh, shit! It's finally hit you, hasn't it?" she says, taking in the look of realisation on my face.

Of course, I *like* like him. I didn't want him to kiss me because I was drunk and confused. I wanted him to kiss me because I *like* him and I hate the thought of him kissing anyone else. It's obvious to me, now, but it's too late to do anything. I'm going on a date on Monday night. Of course, I could cancel but do I want to?

What if I did do something about it, what's to say Jake would see it as anything more than just a good time?

Or what if his Mum is right and he does have a secret girlfriend?

"He can date whoever he wants," I finally say. "It's not like I can say anything. I'm dating."

"He isn't dating anyone, you know that! He obviously likes you. Just tell him you fancy him, too," Laura says, exasperated.

"Okay, what if I do tell him? Jake has already told me he doesn't date. Even if he made an exception and we date for a little bit, what happens when someone else catches his eye? You know how fickle he can be. Then, when it ends - which it inevitably would - we continue to run a business together? Will one of us have to leave? Just because I fancy him and I think about him all the time and want to spend every waking second I have with him doesn't mean I should act on it. The risks are too high."

"I think you're underestimating him. What if you fall in love? You could be happy."

"But what if we don't? It will end and, eventually, I'll lose him. Not to mention it will probably be me who would end up completely heartbroken and have to leave. Losing my dad's life work over a fling? It isn't worth the risk."

"What if you don't do anything about it and lose him anyway? Could you watch him get married? Or have kids? Because you can guarantee he won't be single for the rest of his life."

I suppose that's something I'll have to figure out...

***

Monday comes around quickly and Jake isn't his usually bubbly self. He didn't meet me at the tube station, he didn't reply to any of my texts over the weekend and I don't think he's even looked at me this morning. I don't bring any of that up, though; there's no use rocking the boat any more than I apparently already have. Instead, we get on with our morning in a business-like fashion.

We attend our own meetings, we do our job and that's about it. There's no flirting or talking about anything not related to our work. He doesn't look over at me from his desk with his cheeky grin or mischievous eyes and, by 11 am, I wanted to give him a good shake, to demand that he snaps out of it. I held back because I was too afraid of having to admit my own feelings to him and I really didn't have time to worry about it with everything else going on today.

I had psyched myself up over the weekend and planned to ask him if he wanted me to cancel my date but we hadn't been alone all morning. Sasha and Thomas would come in and out of the office, a bunch of other people come and go dropping paperwork off or picking paperwork up.

I took Laura's advice and downloaded Instagram and so had Jude come to help me set it all up. He showed me our Instagram feed and the amazing rise in engagement we've had because of his campaign. Apparently, the picture of Jake and I in our matching t-shirts brought in the most likes we've had on the page so far. I guess he was right; people like to see behind the scenes.

"What do you fancy doing for lunch today?" I ask Jake when he gets back to our office after his last meeting of the morning. We've eaten lunch together every day for three weeks so it doesn't occur to me that we wouldn't today.

"I'm going to head out and meet some people," he says, shuffling some documents around without looking my way.

"Oh, right. Lovely," I say with disappointment plastered across my face.

"Have you seen the stuff Lou brought in?" he asks, still searching.

"It's just there," I say, pointing towards the shelves by the window. "Going anywhere nice?"

"Huh?" he asks, not really listening to me which is starting to wind me up.

"For lunch? Are you going anywhere nice for lunch?"

"Not really," he says, reading a file that Thomas left on his desk earlier and put it next to the other pile of documents before picking up another and then another.

I can feel myself getting more and more annoyed as I mentally scream at him to just look at me. It doesn't work: He can't read my mind. If he could, he would more than likely be shocked by the expletive thoughts aimed his way.

"Right, well, I'm in back-to-back meetings this afternoon so I probably won't see you until we leave for the day. We'll be ready by six, yeah? I'm sending the instructions down to scheduling at 3 so we'll have plenty of catch-up time after that."

"I have plans after work. I'm leaving at four," he says dismissively.

That's about as much as I can handle. He still refuses to look anywhere close to my direction as he gives me his clipped answers.

"What are you doing, Jake?" I snap in frustration as I shut the office door, planting my hands on my hips as I glare at him.

"I'm not doing anything, Maggie. I have a date after work with someone I met on Saturday night. As per your rules, I'm not permitted to talk to you about it. You can't be mad at me for following your own rules." There's an edge to his voice when he speaks and it cuts me deeper with every word.

Jake has a date and I'm left feeling like a red-hot poker has been shoved deep into my chest cavity.

"Oh, right, well… That's nice. I hope you have a lovely time." Lies, all lies.

I hope he has a shit time.

I feel guilty as soon as the thought enters my mind. I have no right to feel that way when I'm going on a date tonight, too.

He puts his coat on and starts to leave without another word.

"Jake, please," I shout after him and he turns to look at me for the first time. I want to tell him I'll cancel my date but what use is it if he has a date, too? I knew that if we repeated what almost happened on Friday night, it would be a huge mistake.

"What, Maggie? What more do you want from me?" he says, exasperated. It's as though talking to me is a chore. In all the years we didn't speak, he had never looked at me like this, so disconnected, cold and bored. Tears fill my eyes at his icy words. This isn't like him at all and it's killing me.

"Don't do this. Please, don't push me away again. I don't think I can handle it," I beg, desperation oozing from every word as I'm barely clinging on to our friendship with the tips of my fingers.

For a moment, he looks at me and his eyes soften, looking almost sad. Maybe he's feeling as bad about our fight as I am?

"Why are we fighting, Jake? Why do I feel like I'm losing you?"

He doesn't seem to know the answer any more than I do.

"I'm sorry, Maggie," he says, coming to me and kissing

my forehead, pulling me in close to his body as he strokes my hair. I close my eyes at his touch and wrap my arms around his waist. I just want my friend back. I'd do anything to go back to Friday night and change the way things ended. The embrace should be comforting but it's far from it. This feels more like a goodbye than us making up.

He takes a deep breath and I can hear the emotion break in his voice as he speaks.

"I just need a bit of space, that's all. We've spent three weeks in each other's pockets and I love spending time with you, I really do, but-" He cuts off.

But what?

"We can do lunch tomorrow, okay? I just need a night where you don't text me or call me."

He walks out the office, leaving me standing there all alone. I should feel better. He wants to do lunch tomorrow, that has got to mean something, right? Instead, it's like everything has somehow gotten even worse as I watch him leave.

'I just need a night where you don't text me or call me'.

So, that's it? I'm being too full on or something? He needs space? Clearly, we are on two different pages when it came to our friendship.

I sit at my desk, trying to stop the tears that are threatening to fall and dial Laura's number, hoping she has the answers to my problems.

***

Sam is stood outside the restaurant when I arrive later that evening. I guessed it was him due to his right arm being held up in a sling. We introduce ourselves and hit it off straight away. I suppose there's no better icebreaker than having to chop someone's food for them. He seems embarrassed, at first, but then we both start uncontrollably laughing at the bizarre situation and we both seem to get past our initial nerves.

"Last week, did you think I'd be sat here, chopping your food for you on our first date?" I say through tears of laughter.

"I mean, it's a remarkable story, right? I wonder how many first dates start like this."

I have to agree with him there.

"You'll have to excuse my terrible table manners tonight. I can only eat with my left hand which I'm not great at so will probably end up with food all down myself by the end of the evening," he adds. "So, tell me more about what you do. Laura was telling me that you own an Advertising Agency?"

"Co-own, really. My dad and his best friend started the agency back in the early eighties. They decided to retire this year and passed the company to me and Jake. It's been two weeks and we seem to be doing okay."

Other than today's argument, I think.

"Your business partner?"

"Yeah, he's a friend, too. We grew up together since our

parents are close." My heart pulls when I talk about him so I decide to change the subject. "What is it that you do?"

"I'm a children's TV presenter."

Good with kids. Good to know.

"Wow, that's amazing. I bet it's lot of fun." I can see how the job would suit him. From first impressions, he seems wholesome and caring. Those are two great qualities you'd hope to find in a kid's TV host, I imagine.

"We get paid to play games and act around all day. Don't get me wrong, it's so much fun, but the filming is long and tiring. Maybe that's why I'm thirty-five and still single, the long hours," he says, smiling a wide grin and showing his perfectly straight, white teeth.

"I know all about that. Long hours, I mean. We're working on the biggest pitch in the history of our agency so we've been putting a lot of long days in. It's a good job I like my co-workers," I say before realising that probably was a bit more literal than I intended.

Why can't I get that man out of my head? Jake has no business being in there when I'm on a date with a handsome stranger.

"You understand the struggle then" he says smiling again. He's so lovely that it makes me feel guilty, makes me wish I could focus.

As far as first dates go (not that I've had many to compare), this does seem to be going well. It helps that Sam is attractive. He's not at all like Jake. In fact, he couldn't be more different. He's tall with blonde, wavy hair that sweeps down over his forehead and deep brown eyes. Our conversation flows well and we spend most of the evening laughing at each other's stories, particularly my disastrous Tinder date (which he finds hilarious). I suppose that, looking back, I can see the funny side of it.

"I just can't imagine you stood in the street in handcuffs."

"Right?! It was so embarrassing. As if anyone could look at me and see a criminal," I say laughing at my own misfortune. "Anyway, I deleted all the dating apps, they're nothing but trouble."

"Well, that's good to know," he says as his eyes shine over his drink.

He tells me the hilarious story of his broken collarbone and is shocked when I ask if he had a picture of the x-ray and if I could see it. He laughs as I wince at the sight of his bone snapped clearly in two. I'm not sure what I was expecting but it wasn't that. All is most definitely forgiven for standing me up.

As it turns out, the children's TV world is pretty scandalous so he has his fair share of great tales to tell. I can't wait to hear more. There isn't a single moment where we're sat in silence. We talk about our hobbies, likes and dislikes and generally get to know each other. He smiles a lot when he tells me about his family and shows me pictures of his older sister's two young children. It's clear that he adores them, his eyes sparkle when he says their names.

He asks me about Philip, too. I suppose Laura told him about that and I tell him the condensed version of what happened, leaving out all the tragic details and the years that have led me here. Talking about being a widow isn't really first date material. But, what I do tell him, he intently listens to, taking it all in. When I talk so fondly about Philip, there's no sign of jealousy at all. He just wants to know more about the kind of person he was and even asks about the kind of relationship we had.

The whole evening, he was such a gentleman, pulling out my chair and opening doors. He even insisted on walking me home so he knew I was safe, even though he lives half an hour in the other direction.

If I had a checklist, he would tick every box.

Great looking? Check.

Good with kids? Check.

Great job that he loves and plenty of ambition? Check.

Great listener, kind, considerate? Check, check and check.

I'm glad I gave him a second chance because, if I didn't, I wouldn't be having such a lovely time with Sam. The whole situation still begs the question: Would I be having a lovely time with Jake if I didn't answer my phone that night?

"So, this is me," I say as we reach my front door.

"I've had a really nice night," he says, nervously looking at his shoes. "I know it's not the done thing and I'm sure there's a rule on waiting so many days but… do you think I can ask you on a second date?"

"I would love that," I say, my grin matching his.

"We'll, I'm off all week with this," he says, indicating to the sling. "How about I meet you for lunch near your office one day?"

"That sounds great. I will check my meetings and text you tomorrow?" I ask before quickly adding, "Unless there's a rule against that, too?"

Is there a rule? Does it make me look desperate? I should have really Googled the rules of dating.

"Text me tomorrow," he says, smiling as he pulls me in with his good arm to place a soft kiss on my cheek, pausing for a second before kissing me on the mouth.

It's a sweet kiss, soft and delicate. Romantic.

Was it as earth shattering as my almost kiss with Jake? No, but it was pleasant.

I have got to stop comparing the two.

"You should get inside, it's cold," he says once he's pulled away.

"Goodnight, Sam. Thank you, again, for dinner tonight. I had a great time," I say, unable to suppress the smile on my face as I turn away.

I turn and wave as I shut the door but something catches my attention: A black car with tinted windows I hadn't noticed before, sat directly across the road before speeding off down the street. A car that looked a lot like Jake's car. I pull out my phone and dial his number but he doesn't answer which leaves me with even more questions about his behaviour than I already had.

I thought he was out on a date. Does she live close by, is that why he was here? Or was he checking up on me?

I send him a quick text, asking him to call me but I don't expect him to. If he was on a date, he's probably busy.

I let myself into my flat and my phone dings. I was expecting to see Jake's name when I heard the notification but, instead, it's a message from Sam which lifts my spirits again.

Sam: Thanks for giving me a second chance tonight, it was great. Sleep well. X

Sam is a great man and a great catch; I should feel lucky he asked me out on a second date. Whether it was him or not, Jake Mills is not going to ruin this moment for me so I put him to the back of my mind once again. I call Laura (as instructed) to tell her about my fantastic first date with Sam.

CHAPTER NINE

It's been almost 2 weeks since Sam and I went on our first date and we've spoken every day. I really like him. Sam is kind and sweet, he's attractive and a great kisser. On paper, he's everything. In reality, I'm not entirely sure.

I can't shake the feeling that something is missing. At first, I put it down to the ridiculous crush I'd developed on Jake and the fact this whole dating thing is weird for me anyway but, as time goes on, I still find myself looking for more from Sam (which is ridiculous since we've only been on a handful of dates). As my new relationship with Sam slowly grows, my relationship with Jake quickly deteriorates.

The lunch he promised me has been postponed, indefinitely, as he suddenly had an urgent errand to run and says it would be quicker doing it himself than if I went along with him. He no longer answers my phone calls outside of working hours, he doesn't reply to my texts and getting a personal conversation out of him is like getting blood from a stone. The deal I made to spend time with him once a week is apparently void as he didn't even show up to The George last Friday.

James thinks I need to back off and give him the space

he's asked for but I really don't know how to give him more space than I already have.

When we're in the office together, it's like nothing has happened and we've worked hard together to finish our pitch early but that's it. Now, we're back to our own projects and I keep trying to find excuses to talk to him that don't involve me screaming in his face, demanding to know what the hell is going through his mind. I probably would have done so already if it was ever just the two of us but he has reverted to his old ways. He comes in to work late and leaves early, leaving me behind to do the boring jobs that he doesn't want to do, like signing off on payroll or approving our monthly budgets.

So, yeah, I'm madder at him than ever before and I can't do anything about it because, apparently, he needs his 'space'.

I'm surprised to see him sat with James and Helen at our usual table when I arrive at the pub tonight. Sam has gone back to work this week and won't finish his filming until later tonight so we've planned a late dinner, giving him chance to go home and change. Since he said he would meet me here, it'll be the first time he meets my friends and to say I'm anxious is an understatement. We've been dating less than two weeks, a part of me is screaming that this is going too fast but another part is saying, *just go for it*.

"Tonight, is your what... fifth date? In 2 weeks?" Harry asks.

"Yeah, he's met me for lunch a few times, too, but don't really count them as dates."

"You know what that means, right?" Simon chips in.

I just stare blankly, clearly not in on this secret. I never did Google the rules of dating.

"Sex," they say together.

"She doesn't have to have sex with him - they've just met! She doesn't even know him," Jake protests as everyone turns their heads to look at him with raised eyebrows. It's the first time he's even looked my way since I got here an hour ago, let alone spoken to me.

"That's rich, coming from you," I say, defensively. I'm just saying what everyone else was thinking.

The atmosphere shifts and I can tell people are already starting to feel uncomfortable with the tension building between us. I can feel it chipping away at the little resolve I have left and I'm close to breaking point.

"Yeah, well... I'm just saying. You don't have to do it if you don't want to."

"Who said I don't want to? How would you even know?"

"Do you want to?" he snaps back.

"It's none of your business. You are literally the last person who can judge me based on my sex life, Jake."

"But it's okay for you to barely speak to me for eight years based on mine?" he bites back.

"You pushed me away first; that's on you. And how can you say that when you've barely spoken to me these past two weeks?"

"Yeah, well, this is going to be a long seven years and 50 weeks for you."

No-one at the table dares speak a word as Jake and I stare each other down, seething at each other so I'm relieved when my brother breaks the silence.

"Well, I don't want to be part of this conversation so I'm going to the bar and you're coming with me. When you both calm down, you can talk it through like adults because the way you're behaving currently is far from acting your age," James says, pulling Jake from his seat and dragging him towards the bar where they seem to have a heated conversation.

"I'm coming," Laura shouts after them, making her way over to join their conversation.

I huff as I return my attention to Simon and Harry.

"Do you have matching lingerie on?" Harry says as though that argument didn't happen.

"Yes." That makes a change.

"And condoms? Any self-respecting person is always prepared. Do you have any questions?" Simon queries.

"I'm pretty sure I know what I'm doing. Sex is sex. Things can't have changed that much... Right?"

"The basics are the same but you're a little out of practice, hun. I'm sure it'll be fine," Harry says, waving it off.

"The key is having open dialogue. Don't be afraid to let him know when you like something or don't like something," Simon adds, making me think I should be writing notes.

"I'm sure I'll be fine. Anyway, I doubt sex is on the cards. He is still in a lot of pain with his collarbone, after all," I say as I spot Sam walk through the door so I wave to get his attention. "He's here. Please make him feel welcome," I beg as James, Jake and Laura finally join our table again. I aim my remarks directly at Jake because you never know what side of him you're going to get, lately.

It's awkward when Sam greets me with a kiss on the mouth and a wide smile before I introduce him to everyone but I put that down to my nerves and the anger that is still floating around inside of me. Jake is still tense from our argument, his jaw set in a straight line, but he shakes Sam's hand, none the less, maybe squeezing a little bit too hard. Sam places his arm back around my waist, pulling me in to his side as he makes small talk with my friends. Jake doesn't say anything when he leaves the table and disappears to the back of the pub.

Guess I'll sort things out with him later, then.

James looks at me apologetically: He knows more than he is letting on. I want to ask him about it but it's not a conversation I want to have with Sam around.

As soon as it's socially acceptable, Sam and I excuse ourselves and head out for dinner.

"Are you okay?" Sam asks as we walk to the tube station.

"I'm fine. Jake and I just had a little disagreement before you arrived," I say, putting it mildly.

"Well, I'll try my best to distract you," he says, stopping

162

to kiss me in the street. I smile but it's forced, not that I let Sam know that.

"Let's just eat and enjoy our night."

***

After dinner, we take a moonlit walk across Westminster Bridge. Tourists are still out taking pictures, busses full of people going anywhere and everywhere. It would be romantic if I could focus for longer than five seconds. Instead, I can't get Jake out of my head. Conversation with Sam doesn't flow as easily tonight as it has done previously which is completely my fault.

I compare him to how it used to be with Jake before we fell out again. Sam doesn't make me laugh as much as Jake does. I don't feel as comfortable with him as I do with Jake. He doesn't make my heart race like Jake does: Even when we're arguing, I still have those butterflies. As we reach the tube station, my stomach is tied in knots because I know I have got to end things with Sam before they get too far. My mind is swirling as I think about it and I have no idea how to do this.

"So, did you want to come back to my place? It's only three stops away on the Piccadilly line," Sam says, winding his arm around my waist and kissing me again but it doesn't make me feel anything. It's pleasant, yes, but there's no deeper connection and I don't think there ever was.

"I'm sorry. I think I'm just going to go home. I've really

enjoyed spending time with you but there's just something missing, something that I can't give you," I say honestly. "You're a lovely man, Sam, you'll make someone incredibly happy. I really hope you find what you're looking for, I'm just sorry I'm not it."

He looks at me intently and I can see that he understands.

"Thank you for being honest. I hope you work things out with your partner, too. I can see how much it's upset you," he says, giving me a platonic kiss on the cheek and walking down to his platform.

I slowly make my way to my own platform, in no rush to go home alone.

He's right about Jake. I know he will still be at The George. He doesn't usually leave until last orders with the rest of us so I decide I need to face him, once and for all.

We're sorting this out tonight, whether he likes it or not.

***

The entire journey back, I think about what I'll say but all that goes out of the window when Jake is the first person I see as I enter the busy pub. As soon as he meets my eye, I'm seething, the anger and rage I have suppressed for two weeks bubbling to the surface like it did before. This time, I know I won't be able to stop myself.

I ignore the greetings and the confusion from my friends who weren't expecting to see me again tonight and I square up to Jake who stands at the edge of the table. I doubt I'm as threatening to him as I think I am, especially since he is at least a foot taller than me.

"Why the hell did you have to get in my head?" I snap at him as soon as I reach the table, shocking him. "Sam is a great man. He has a fantastic job; he is passionate and generous. He has goals and aspirations and a life plan."

"Then why aren't you in his bed? Wasn't that the idea?" he says, taking a step towards me.

His piercing eyes meet mine, sending shock waves throughout my entire body. This feeling between us, right now, is what I was missing with Sam. Chemistry, physical attraction, fireworks.

"'She doesn't have to have sex with him, she doesn't even know him'," I say in a terrible impression of him. It doesn't help that I'm slightly out of breath from all the rage. "You got in my head; you know you did. You did it on purpose. He was gorgeous and perfect-"

"If he's so perfect, Maggs, where is he?"

"I liked him!" I say, losing my temper once more. "I liked him a lot but all I've been able to think about throughout my entire date was that something was wrong and I couldn't work out what it was. I spent most of the night trying to justify what you said. In the end, the only thing I could see clearly was you. I tried to put you out of my mind and remember how I usually feel with Sam but, instead, all I could think about was how *you* make me feel!"

I don't dare look at anyone other than Jake; they all heard

my confession.

Shit.

"Made. I meant how you *made* me feel... Earlier... When you told me not to have sex with him," I say as I awkwardly try to backtrack and catch my breath again.

Silence.

We both stand, staring at each other. Neither of us dare speak.

Our friends are looking between us like they're watching Wimbledon. Even some of the neighbouring tables are watching, waiting for one of us to speak, for one of us to address what I said.

He just looks at me, his mouth slightly open in shock.

"Is that what you meant, Maggs? Or did you mean it the first way?" he asks, his face no longer confrontational. Now, he just looks confused and maybe a little hopeful.

"Get out of my head," I shout, panicking and practically running for the door, not really knowing where else to go with this conversation. My heart threatens to jump out of my throat as I storm out, doing my best not to turn around when he eventually shouts my name in his gorgeously rough voice.

I hate how much I want him right now. I hate how I didn't kiss him when I had the chance. I hate how I can't bring myself to tell him how I really feel about him.

He catches up to me before I reach the street, grabbing my hand before I reach the ivy archway in the entrance, the fairy light-covered pergola twinkling above us like stars. It starts to rain. This could be a really romantic movie moment if it weren't freezing and I wasn't getting soaked to the bone. If this were a movie, he would spin me to face him, bury his hand in my hair and tell me that he loves me. We'd share a passionate kiss in the rain, complete with tears of joy and then the credits would roll. We'd live happily ever after.

This isn't a movie. This is real life and the reality is that rainwater is going in my eyes and my mascara must be running, my clothes are already saturated from the sudden downpour and are now sticking to me. I don't even want to imagine what state my hair is in. Far from sexy, that's for sure.

He turns me around to face him as I let out a long breath but he's still holding my hand out at arm's length.

"Please, Maggs. I'm sorry I said that. I wasn't judging you. I know I'm a hypocrite but I just wanted you to be sure before you jumped into bed with someone you barely know."

He pushes his soaking wet hair away from his face and wipes the water from his forehead with his sleeve. Why does he have to look so handsome when I probably look like a drowned rat?

"It's not like I'm a virgin. You don't need to defend my honour." I hear people snickering from the smoking shelter. Very mature.

"That's not what I'm doing."

"I'm not a delicate, little flower that you need to protect."

"Believe me, I know. I've spent the last 8 years stuck on

the end of your stinger," he says, trying to make me smile with one of his charming grins as he steps closer to me. Our bodies are now mere inches apart and he's still holding my hand.

"I'm going home, Jake. You should go back inside. I'll see you Monday," I say, my voice sounding small. I don't move to leave; I don't think I'm able to step away from his warmth that I still crave.

"What about our plans tomorrow?" he asks, looking hurt.

"We have no plans, Jake. If this conversation had never happened, you would have cancelled them anyway. Right now, I can barely call you a friend which kills me because I had become so dependent on your friendship. Maybe that was our problem all along."

"Maggs, it's got nothing to do with that. I'm sorry. Tell me how to make it better, give me a chance to make it up to you," he pleads with me. He tenderly pushes my wet hair from my face with his free hand, his warm fingers leaving a heat trail as I lean into his touch, wanting to be closer but knowing that I shouldn't. His other hand still clings to mine as though he doesn't want us to separate any more than I do. "I'm sorry for the way I've acted these two weeks, I'm sorry for what I said earlier. I didn't want to hurt you. Please, believe me."

"I'm sure you are sorry but where was this attitude two weeks ago when I begged you not to push me away? That's the part that hurt me. You promised me you wouldn't and you did it anyway." I close my eyes while I try to compose myself.

"Remember when you asked me to give you space and I did? For two whole weeks, I gave you space when you probably didn't deserve it," I say, unable to keep my eyes from filling up when I look at him one last time.

Finally, I gather enough courage to step out of his hold. His shoulders are slouched, his hands stuffed in his pockets.

"I'm tired of it all, Jake. I'm tired of your mood swings and never knowing where I stand with you. I need a break from it all and maybe you should use the time to decide how you actually want me in your life."

I walk away, tears stinging my eyes but I am determined not to let him see me cry over our argument.

This time, he doesn't follow me. Instead, he lets me go.

I hear lighter footsteps running up behind me. "Maggie, wait," Laura links her arm through mine when she catches up and we walk back to my flat together in silence. She doesn't push me to talk about it or ask what was said.

She waits for me in my living room as I have a long, hot shower to try and warm up again. It's not until I change into my 'Do you even golf' T-shirt and sit down next to her on the sofa with my legs tucked beneath me that the first tears fall. She still doesn't speak, just moves me so my head is in her lap and strokes my hair gently, letting me cry until my tears dry up.

***

I wake up early the next morning, still on my sofa with Laura. I apologised to her for my breakdown, thanked her for staying with me and put on my best smile to convince her I was okay. Then, as soon as she left to go to work, the smile slipped, my chest caved in and I crawled into bed.

I'm so grateful for my best friend being here but I wished, more than anything, that I could talk to Philip. Philip always knew what to say when I was sad, he always knew what I should do when I had a problem. He always supported me, no matter what.

Would he know what I should do about Jake? Would he support my decision? Or would he be disappointed in me over the way things have turned out between us? That's the thing about losing someone you didn't think you could live without. You constantly think about the 'ifs'. You yearn for their answers that will never come, pine for their opinions and long for their advice.

"I know it's been a few weeks since I spoke to you. I thought I was doing better, I thought I was moving forward. It was what I wanted but I need you, right now. I need to know, what should I do?" I say as I curl up into a ball under my duvet.

Philip doesn't answer me. He never does. He can't. He isn't here anymore.

It's just me, left to face my problems by myself.

I don't want to be alone.

It's been four days since our fight in the rain and I have made the best attempt to avoid Jake. He didn't try to call me and just sent me one text message that shattered me all over again. I left it unanswered.

Jake: Maggs, I miss you. x

For the entirety of yesterday and all this morning, we've both had separate, back-to-back meetings to catch up on things we had put aside to work on the Stephenson's pitch so I haven't physically seen him, Until now, when he stands outside of our office on Tuesday lunchtime.

He walks in and closes the door behind him, something we only do when we don't want to be overheard.

"Maggie, can we talk?"

"Is it work related?"

"You know it's not."

"Then no. I have a lunch date I need to get to," I say as I stand from my chair. He quickly moves to slide between me and my desk, blocking me from my handbag.

I stand with my arms crossed, staring at him. Why is he doing this to me? Why is he torturing me like this?

"Laura is running late. Sasha asked me to tell you," he says, grinning at me with his eyes glimmering in the light.

"I had to endure the silent treatment from you for two whole weeks. Why should I let you off so soon?"

He leans against my desk, propping himself up with his hands on the edge. Yes, I notice he's tensing his muscles at me; he's literally pulling out the big guns in an attempt at getting me to talk to him. It's working; I can feel my anger at him melting away just like it did the other night when he looked so vulnerable in the rain.

Two can play at this game.

"Okay, let me ask you one question," I say, coming so close to him that I'm now standing between his legs. He lifts his hand to rest on my side, his thumb dangerously close to grazing my under boob. I lean forward and arch my back so my boobs push into him. I'm close enough that my mouth is level with his ear, one hand gripping his muscular shoulder and the other winding around his back.

Lowering my voice slightly, I continue. I can already see the goosebumps on his neck and the hairs on the back of my own stand up. "Think back to Friday night and the opinion you had on my sex life. What would you have said if it was you I wanted to sleep with? Would that have been okay with you?"

"I, uh.. Shit, what?" he whimpers and stutters, caught off guard. His Adam's apple bobs in his throat and his fingertips dig so hard into my ribs that it almost hurts. Jake Mills is nervous and maybe a little turned on.

I know I am.

I grab my bag from behind his back and straighten up while he is momentarily distracted. He clears his throat as I pat his cheek, thoroughly pleased with myself, before I move away from him. He doesn't move from the spot I leave him in.

"That's not fair," he shouts as I leave our office, waving at him behind me. "I can play dirty, too, Maggie. You may have won this round but, believe me, you'll be talking to me again by the end of the day."

Shit. I'm actually sweating at his threat.

***

When I return to my office after lunch Jake, is nowhere to be seen but, sat on my desk, is an orange and pink gift bag that reminds me of Bassets Fruit Salad Chews, my favourite sweets. I pick out the card that's buried inside and slowly slide it out of the envelope. I smile as I see the familiar writing.

I'm a shithead, some may even say an asshat.

I let out a small laugh at the sentiment and take another look in the bag. I pull out a gift box and open it. My chest fills with warmth when I pull out a brand-new pair of white sand shoes.

"I've missed that smile, Maggs," he says quietly as he closes the door behind him.

He doesn't come any closer. Instead, he stands awkwardly with his hands stuffed in his pockets like he does when he's nervous.

"Thank you. I'm impressed that you got the right size," I say as I go to him. "The bag kind of makes me want some sweets though. You know they're my favourite," I say with a smile, letting him know that his thoughtful gift is appreciated.

He skips over to his desk and pulls out a huge jar with a big pink and orange bow. "I knew you'd say that so I got you this, too." I open the jar and see a mixture of Fruit Salad and Blackjack sweets.

"You really do know how to soften me up, don't you?" I say as I walk towards him and pull him in for a sweet cuddle, having to stand on my tip toes. Finally, he has realised the way to break me down is to be himself. I take a step back again and put the jar down on his desk.

"I am sorry, Maggie. Please, say you forgive me. I didn't mean it when I said we needed space from each other. I don't even know why I said it, I regretted it straight away. And I lied about that date, I made it all up. I guess I didn't want to seem like I was pathetically alone when you seemed so happy."

I take it all in, not really understanding why he would lie about having a date. I don't ask him why he was outside of my flat either, although I'm desperate to know. I don't think he's ready to tell me.

"I do forgive you but, please, don't do that to me again. We're supposed to be friends - best friends, even. Best friends don't shut down and push each other away for no apparent reason."

"I promise. I've missed you so much," he says, pulling me

towards him again and wrapping his strong arms around me. I feel safe and warm again and all the tension that was between us feels like it had just been a bad dream.

I know things between us have changed on my part and it's something I need to deal with myself but I have already decided not to let that change anything between us or the work we do together. I just need to stay strong and keep the promise that I made myself, that I would lock those feelings up inside like everything else.

"I missed you, too, Jake," I say as he buries his face in my neck. "And, as a celebration of us being friends again-"

"Best friends!"

I smile at the correction. "Best friends... I'll let you cook me dinner tonight because, quite honestly, I've missed your cooking."

"Ah, you're using me for my cooking skills," he says with a chuckle, the brightness restored in his eyes. "I would be honoured."

CHAPTER TEN

The following Saturday, I was woken up by the incessant buzzing of Jake ringing my doorbell. I groan as I pull myself out of bed, checking the clock on my way past.

Just like the last time we argued and made up, we fell back into our usual stride again; eating dinner together most nights, texting and speaking all the time, playing games of pool that get more and more sexually charged as the weeks pass.

"So, I know it's early."

"It's 8 am on Saturday. I thought that, when you told me not to work weekends anymore, I'd at least get a lie in or something."

"Has anyone ever told you you're cranky when you wake up?" he says, walking past me to my bedroom. "I know we don't have official plans today but I need you to spend the day with me," he says making himself all too comfortable, resting his hands behind his head as he lazes on my bed before pressing the remote that lifts the TV from the base.

"Okay... Why?"

"I can't say. It's a surprise but just trust me here, I know you'll love it. Get ready and we'll leave when you're done."

"Where are we going?"

"No more questions. Get ready," he says, getting up to steer me into my bathroom.

"Okay, okay!"

It takes less than an hour from me getting ready before we make it to our surprise destination in Greenwich. Jake has brought me to the Royal Observatory. Our parents planned to bring us all here as kids but, the day we were supposed to come, my brother woke up with chicken pox so we had to cancel. Every school holiday that followed, Mum would promise she would bring me here but things always got in the way. Eventually, I grew up and we never got around to doing it.

It's a chilly day with a little wind but at least the rain has held off - so far. We talk as we take a slow walk-through Greenwich Park towards the steep hill leading up to the observatory. When we eventually reach the top of the incline, we make our way to the entrance where Jake produces the tickets he had pre-booked for us.

The lady on the ticket desk welcomes us with a friendly smile, hands me our map and show timetable which Jake immediately takes off me and shoves into his pocket.

"We don't need this; I've already got it all memorised. I thought we could start with the Meridian Line."

"Lead the way then, Mr Tour Guide."

"Put one foot here and the other there," he says, indicating to either side of the stainless-steel line built into the floor as he faces me. "You are officially in two places at once"

I smile at him. "Just like in 'A Walk to Remember'."

"I have no idea what that is."

"It's a book by Nicholas Sparks. They made a movie with Mandy Moore. It was good."

He just looks at me blankly.

"Mandy Moore's character has terminal cancer and she falls in love with a boy called Landon. Basically, she has this bucket list and one item is to be in two places at the same time. Landon takes her to the town line and, when she puts a foot either side, she is in two places at once. It's so romantic."

"It sounds tragic."

"It is. She dies in the end. Someone usually does die in a Nicholas Sparks book so you should expect it but it doesn't make it any less heart-breaking."

He smiles at me softly, making me feel ever so slightly flustered.

"So, tell me about this line then. I suppose you've been studying," I say, cocking an eyebrow at him. I know he will have read every piece of information he could find online; he likes to be the fountain of all knowledge and this is the perfect time to show off.

"Of course, I have. This is the Meridian Line. It's nought degrees longitude. It's the main line that runs down the centre of the earth like the equator but vertical. Right now, your left foot is in the Eastern Hemisphere and your right foot is in the Western Hemisphere. At night, there is a green laser that marks out the line across London. It should be dark by the time we leave so we'll be able to see it."

"That's pretty cool. Here, I'll take a photo," I say, pulling my phone out to take a photo of our feet straddling the line. He's wearing his worn-out Vans and I'm wearing my new, white sandshoes.

I look up to find him smiling down at me again.

"What?" I ask. His smile is contagious.

"Come on, let's go to the planetarium. There's a show starting soon."

***

We spend the afternoon wandering through the observatory, visiting their different exhibits and dropping in and out of planetarium shows about the Solar System and the Milky Way. We talk about the new facts we learn and Jake laughs hysterically when I voice my frustrations about Pluto's declassification as a planet.

As we walk around, he puffs his chest out, proudly reciting facts he's learnt in preparation for our day out and it is the cutest thing I've ever seen. I could listen to him for hours, just talking about the Great Equatorial Telescope or the famous Harrison Clocks. We stop for lunch on the terrace of the Parkside café, looking out over Greenwich Park. The sun finally broke through the clouds and you can Central London in the distance.

"Shall we head back into London and get some dinner somewhere?" I ask after our final planetarium show, the voice on the speaker announcing that they are closing soon.

"Not yet. Let's just wait 20 minutes so we don't get stuck in the crowd. There's nothing worse than hundreds of people cramming onto the tube." He suddenly seems distracted as he types a quick message on his phone.

"Yeah, okay, makes sense."

We take a seat on a wooden bench outside the planetarium and Jake is unusually fidgety when, finally, a man wearing a Royal Observatory polo shirt approaches us.

"Hey, man," he says to Jake.

"Hey, Carl. How's things? How's the family?" They exchange a manly shoulder-clapping hug.

"I'm good, Stace is good. She's pregnant. Our third kid."

"Sounds like a handful."

"Yeah, but it's so worth it when they smile at you with their cute, little dimples and tiny teeth and stuff," he replies with a chuckle and a smile. "Who would have thought I'd turn into such a soft, family man."

"This is Maggie, James' sister," Jake introduces us. "Carl lived in the same uni halls as me and James."

"Ah, you're 'Crazy Carl'?" I ask with an understanding grin. I've heard many stories about Crazy Carl over the years from

James. He got the nickname during their first freshers' week when he tried to jump his skateboard over a Nissan Micra. He ended up fracturing both wrists but insisted it was worth it because he got a cool nickname and the video was played on *'You've Been Framed'*. Apparently, he did a lot of crazier stuff over the years but, looking at the 'family man' in front of us, the only thing that seems crazy to me is that it's the same person.

"I haven't heard that name for years. I assume your brother told you all about the mischief we used to get into?" He laughs, unlocking the door to the planetarium door next to us.

"Something like that. You're a bit of an urban legend in our house," I say with a grin.

"I would like to say it's all lies but it's probably all true," he says, nudging Jake. "Everything is ready, man. You can head right in. I'll give you a call next week, get a lads night booked in before the baby arrives."

Jake stands aside to let me through as he thanks Carl and I give Jake a suspicious look as I look around the room. The night sky twinkles on the domed ceiling above us and there's not another guest in sight.

"Okay, so I might have done a thing," he says.

"You might have done a thing? Does that include booking the planetarium after hours?"

"Okay, so… Yeah, I did a really big thing," he says with a sheepish grin. "And I hope you like it so sit down and enjoy."

He leads me to a reclined seat in the middle of the circular room where we sit down in the big, theatre chairs and lean back to watch the night sky move above us. The image starts to move, showing the night sky in all its glory and zooming in on various planets, stars and constellations. We sit quietly together, watching the show, listening to the serene music. Neither of us break the silence; we just enjoy the calm sounds and the bright images of space.

The show we watch is different to the other shows we've sat through today; there is no commentary and a lot more astronomical jargon used when pointing out stars and constellations. I don't really understand most of it but it doesn't ruin the experience. I have always felt something so calming about watching the stars. Whenever I was stressed out about school, exams, or homework, I'd sit in the garden and look to the sky. Even if it were a cloudy night, I'd sit out there for hours, willing the clouds to move so I could see.

I would always feel refreshed, as though room had been created in my brain so I was finally able to sort through my thoughts and find the answers I needed.

I wonder if I'll find the answers I've been searching for here.

Philip had a small telescope that we would take out to his tree house on clear nights. He loved everything about space; he had mountains of books and magazines on every subject and dreamed of studying the night sky at the Royal Observatory as a career one day. He was always so passionate about it, yet I'd forgotten all about it until now, as I sit here and think about how much he'd love this.

I look to my left and Jake has his eyes trained on the screens. He doesn't notice me looking at him or, at least, he doesn't react to it until I take his hand in mine, entwining my fingers through his. He squeezes my hand with a smile and I turn my attention back to the ceiling.

The video slows down before zooming in and pausing on a bright star in the distance. A textbook appears next to it and I carefully read it, feeling Jakes eyes on me. I gasp as I absorb the information.

This live image was taken by the Royal Observatory Greenwich at 00:01 on January 1ˢᵗ 2013 and presents the star formerly known as JPB1109-96.

The international Star Registry has been updated and, as of January 10ᵗʰ 2021, this star will be named Philip's Lucky Star in memory of the late Philip Matthews. Loving husband, son, brother and friend.

Tears are streaming down my face as I take in the words on the screen.

"Did you do this?"

"Shit. I'm sorry, I thought you might like it. I remember how into space Philip was," Jake says in a panic.

"Jake," I say as I sit up to look at him properly, taking both of his hands in mine and gently kissing his knuckles. "I love it. These are happy tears, I promise. And you're right, Philip would love it, too."

He visibly relaxes as he wipes away my tears with his sleeve. "I'm relieved. For a second, I thought I had messed up again. I have the certificate and things at home for you. I thought this would be a nice touch and Carl owes me a lifetime of favours so I called one in."

"This is the most thoughtful thing anyone has ever done for me. I don't even know how you did it."

"I did nothing, really. Carl trailed through hours of archived footage to find this star so we could name it. It was a new star that was discovered on the night of the accident," he pauses for a moment as I take it all in. "I noticed that, whenever something is bothering you, you automatically go to play with your wedding rings. Did you know that?"

"I haven't noticed it but, now you've mentioned it, I suppose I do. They were the last thing to connect me to him. The only thing that I kept," I say, a fresh batch of tears falling from my eyes.

After wearing my wedding ring and engagement ring for so long after he died, they became a part of me. After all, they we're once a part of him, too, a symbol of our love and our union. It's no surprise that they became a safety net for me, comforting and a reminder of how lucky I have been. Even now, my finger has been permanently changed by them, indented at the exact place my rings sat. Every day since I took them off, I notice less and less but that doesn't mean I don't still look for them for support.

I'd never expressed any of that to Jake. I never once spoke about the importance of my rings or why I kept them on for so long after Philip died. I didn't have to explain it, Jake got it. He knew me well enough to know how important they were to me. It was touching how he noticed when I took them off for the first time, even after spending barely any time in my company for over 10 years.

"Now, you have this. He's up there whenever you need him, all you need to do is look up," he says, tightly clutching my hand once more, effortlessly comforting me when I need him to.

***

When I finally finished crying and thanking Jake over and over in the planetarium, we made our way home to get changed, ready for the gig Helen got us tickets to tonight.

I quickly re-apply my make-up (since I cried most of it off) and throw on a red skater dress and my chunky Louboutin boots. He picks me up an hour later and we share a taxi to Evil Eye, a secret underground rock'n'roll nightclub in Shoreditch that you need a password to gain entry to.

Everyone is already there when we arrive. They aren't surprised to hear that Jake named a star after Philip; I suppose he'd already told them he was planning on doing it and had to ask Laura for some information. I still can't quite get over it myself and I almost feel like a lovesick puppy as I stare up at him from the comfort of his side while he talks.

Helen, Laura and I take our seats at the long, wooden table and send the others to get the drinks in. It's all a ruse so we can have some girl talk without having to talk in code or worry about what we say.

"This place is so cool. How did you get these tickets, anyway?" I ask Helen, looking around the room.

The walls are painted black and the roof is coated with sound proofing foam. Tributes to punk bands decorate the walls.

"I went to drama school with Nicki, she's the drummer in the band we're here to see," she says, sipping her flavoured gin through a tiny straw. "They toured with the band Evil Eye a few years ago on this huge world tour. Now, they've just put out a new album and they're trying a few local gigs to see if there's interest for a bigger tour."

"Bloody Hell, they know Evil Eye? The band this place was named after?" Laura says, shouting to be heard over the music. "Mackenzie is incredible and really famous. I wonder what happened to her; she just seemed to drop off the face of the earth."

"They were so good. Nicki said one of the band members had a drug problem and they didn't want to continue without him. One of the other guys in the band married the bass player and she got pregnant and didn't want to tour anymore," Helen explains.

"So, anyway, before the boys get back, tell us more about your day at the Observatory."

"We had a really nice time," I say, smiling over at Jake who winks back at me while he leans against the bar, making my heart skip.

"Was it romantic?"

"I don't know what it was, Helen. I know it was nice, though. I really like spending time with him and he's not an insufferable as I once thought. I suppose, for me, it felt romantic but it doesn't help that I can't get over my silly crush. I think he was just being a nice friend, though, it's probably not the same for him as it is for me."

"How do you know? Why not make a move and see what happens?" Laura says. "Tonight is the perfect night. We're in a dark nightclub and we can keep James out the way so it's not weird. There will be dancing and drinking. It's the perfect opportunity to stick your tongue down his throat."

"How many drinks have you had?" I ask through a laugh.

"Enough that I've asked Jake to bring you two extremely strong gin cocktails so you can catch up. What do you say? Are you going to make a move?"

"For starters, I've told you several reasons why that's a bad idea and second, if Jake Mills wanted to kiss me, there have been plenty opportunities for him to do so."

"Like the time he went to kiss you and you pulled away?" Laura says with raised eyebrows.

"What?!" Helen says, almost choking on her drink. "When did that happen?"

"A few weeks ago. We had been out with some people from work and he was walking me home."

"He went to kiss you and you. Pulled. Away?" Helen looks horrified.

"Yeah, then she arranged a date with Sam in front of him," Laura says with an eye roll, throwing me further under the bus.

"Okay, okay. In hindsight, that was a bad idea but we're finally over that. Normality has resumed for us."

Helen looks at me like I've grown an extra head. "Jake tried to kiss you and you pulled away? What the hell is wrong with you? I can say this because I am extremely comfortable in my relationship with James and he would likely agree anyway but Jake is smoking hot. I have seen him without a shirt on multiple occasions. All I will say is 'wow'. You need to get on that."

The guys make their way back to our table and put a stop to our conversation. I know the girls won't let it lie and, as Jake slides his arm around my shoulder so he can speak in my ear above the music, I think for a second. Maybe they're right. All of that still doesn't take away the risks of getting involved with Jake. No matter how brief of a fling it would be, the risks far outweigh the benefits.

"What if we do some fishing first? I'll be sneaky so he won't have a clue what's going on, I promise," Laura suggests when we go to the loos later that night. The strong cocktails and cheap pints are clearly working because, for some reason, I agree.

I know I shouldn't mix my drinks; it makes me do stupid stuff.

"Maggie, I've had an idea and I want everyone's opinion," she says when we return to the table, waiting for the headlining band to start. "There's a new dating app which I want to try for you. You basically advertise your friend for a blind date. I would set up the profile and, based on the info I put in, you'll be matched with a date based on the info their friend puts in."

"Laura!" I protest.

She's trying to goad Jake into action, in front of everyone, including my brother.

"Yes!" Harry exclaims. "I'll help with the profile."

"That sounds bloody amazing," James says with a devilish grin. "What do you think, Jake?"

Great, he's in on it, too. My brother is now trying to pimp me out to his best friend: Not embarrassing at all. Helen shrugs apologetically as I meet her eye. I know she can't keep secrets from him.

"You should go for it."

I stare at Jake and my heart breaks ever so slightly. I knew this was a bad idea. He's confirmed what I was thinking: Our friendship means something different for both of us.

"Do it," I say, turning to face to Laura who is sat opposite me.

Clearly, she wasn't expecting that response as she huffs at

Jake and drags me to the bar even though we just came back with full drinks.

"What did I say?" I hear Jake ask as we walk away.

"You're an idiot," Helen says to him, quickly following behind us.

"I told you, Laura. You all need to just back off. Jake doesn't like me so I just need to get over my silly crush and I can't do that if you keep pushing things that don't want to be pushed."

"I'm sorry but I know this isn't what he wants. I was just trying to get him to admit it to you or, at the very least, to himself."

"Let's get started on that app. Don't worry about Jake, we'll find you someone nice to get over him with," Helen says, squeezing my hand.

***

By the time the headline band comes back on later that evening, Laura, Helen and I are suitably wasted. Laura was right; these cocktails are strong.

To take my mind off Jake, we danced for what feels like hours so my legs and feet ache but I never want to stop. There's something about dancing with your friends to good music that's so freeing.

It works: I don't think about Jake once. Instead, I focus on what's right here in front of me in this exact moment.

"You look happy, Maggie," Laura says in my ear as we

take a drink break. "It's great to see."

"I'm starting to remember who I was before the accident." I didn't realise how lost I was but, standing here with music thumping around us, the lights dancing around dark the room and my best friend grinning back at me, it dawns on me how much I've missed over the years. All that time I stayed home has been wasted, instead of going out clubbing or the nights I worked late rather than going to concerts with my friends. I couldn't even face anything more than going to the local pub for a couple of hours a week.

I can see it all clear as day; my reduced anxiety, my less frequent bouts of depression and anger. I feel better physically, too. I don't have an urge to tap my fingers or toes to distract me from my thoughts and feelings. My back doesn't ache from slouching in uncomfortable situations because nothing about my life in the past month has been uncomfortable.

Now, the only time I experience heart palpitations is when Jake looks at me with his intensely-blue eyes and handsome smile.

My heart swells when I look around at our growing circle filled with my friends and family, carefree and happy. Simon and Harry are wrapped in their new lovers' bubble and Helen is currently on my brothers lap, drunkenly telling him that she loves him (which is, at first, cute but, as soon as she sticks her tongue in his mouth, I want to dry heave).

"I'm glad we're all friends again. They don't need an ego boost so don't tell them I said this but I've missed Jake and James.

And I love spending time with Helen," Laura says, grabbing my attention once more as we take a break by the edge of the dance floor. I feel a pang of guilt when I think of how divided we were until a few weeks ago.

"I've missed them, too. I just wish I knew what happened for everything to fall apart in the first place. Although, I have a strong feeling it might have something to do with me."

"There's no use dwelling on the past, Maggie. It won't change anything. We both know that." I know she's thinking of Philip when she says that as she can't hide the look of pain from her pretty features. I know she misses him just as much as I do. "We better go dance again before we start crying. We can save that for the journey home over a dirty kebab or something," she adds with her beautiful smile shining bright once more.

Jake comes and stands between us, his back leaning on the railing that separates us from the dance floor. Laura begrudgingly leaves us as they stare each other down. She's apparently still annoyed with him but she finally gives him a smile and skips away to join the others.

I've barely seen him tonight since he spotted some of the guys from his team and had been talking to them. I thought about going over there and saying 'hi' but Laura wanted to dance so I took the opportunity to avoid him for a little while.

"You look like you're having fun," he observes, leaning into my ear and sending an involuntary shiver down my spine. I can't help but lean into him as he stands next to me, his fingers aimlessly trailing a pattern down my arm, a gesture so comforting and natural to us. I'm more aware of how his touch makes me feel, now. How I crave (more along the lines of a physical need for closeness) to feel him touch me and hold me.

"Yeah, I am. The band are good. Helen knows the drummer and, apparently, she's single. You should ask her to set you up." Maybe that last part was a bit unnecessary but I wanted to try for myself, to see if I can goad him into action or even just convince myself that things are completely one sided. Moments like this - our closeness - confuse things even more for me.

I don't think about how it would make me feel if I had to watch him hook up with some other girl. Especially someone more in his league than me.

I'm thirty years old and have kissed two men in my entire life. Slept with one. Jake is way more experienced and I imagine he expects more from potential love interests, a lot more than I can offer him. My lack of experience has never bothered me before but, when you look at his track record, it's hard not to feel like a complete loser.

"Is that what you want? You're telling me you want Laura to set you up with some random guy and you want me to hook up with a girl in a band neither of us even know?" he asks, stepping away and creating distance between us. He's on the defence.

"Is that what you want?" I ask, turning his question on him. Of course, I don't want him hooking up with the super attractive, rock star goddess on stage. If I'm being honest with myself, she's more in his league than I am but there's no way I'm telling him that.

"Shit. No, Maggs. I don't want that. Why can't you just tell me how you feel? Why do we have to go backwards and forwards like this? It gets us nowhere. If you want me to hook up with the drummer, just say so and I'll hook up with the drummer, if it'll make you feel better." I don't reply so he continues. "Just say the words if that's what *you* really want."

"What's that supposed to mean?"

"You know what I mean." He sounds annoyed. "Just tell me what you want. Tell me how you feel."

"I don't know what *you* want *me* to say," I shout back at him, confused.

We stand for a moment, fuming as we look at each other, neither of us daring to speak first. What would I even say? That his charm and flirting have finally broken down my walls, that every day I spend with him makes me like him even more? That every day I don't see him, I spend missing him and thinking about him? There's no way I can say that, no matter how many gin cocktails and cheap pints I've had.

"You're killing me, Maggs," he says as he rubs the back of his neck, growls and walks away, leaving me alone in a cloud of confusion.

I stand for a second to try and gather my thoughts which isn't easy when my brain feels like it's stuck in a washing machine. My head is swirling with what we said and the things that are still unspoken. How did we get from harmless flirting to fighting again?

I come up with a million better ways the conversation could have gone, things I should have said, things I wish he had said.

"Come on," James says as he comes to retrieve me from the spot where I still stand, watching Jake walk away. "He'll cool off."

When we get back to the table, he's nowhere to be seen and Helen tells us he's left. I don't hear from him again until the show ends.

Jake: I'm sorry, Maggs. x

It's a loaded message with several possible meanings. Sorry for leaving? Sorry for arguing? Sorry for the mixed signals?

I start to type out a reply but think better of it before I press send. I'm drunk, clearly emotionally unstable since the sight of his name on my phone caused tears to form in my eyes. I don't want to cause us more trouble than we're already in.

All I want to do now is go home and curl up in my nice, warm bed and not think about Jake Mills.

CHAPTER ELEVEN

The morning after the gig last weekend, Jake brought me a coffee along with the certificate of registration for Philip's star which he'd had framed. Neither one of us mentioned our argument from the previous night. We watched TV together in the living room, ordered in lunch and I cooked our dinner that evening.

All the while, we talked about regular things like how good the band was last night and who we thought H was after we finally caught up with the latest series of *'Line of Duty'*.

What I really wanted to ask him was what he meant last night.

'Why can't you just tell me how you feel.'

'Why do we have to go backwards and forwards like this?'

I wanted to tell him what I really thought of our argument, of why I suggested he hook up with the bloody drummer, why I agreed to let Laura set me up on a blind date with a complete stranger when, really, I wanted him.

I didn't tell him any of that.

I wanted to ask what he meant when he apologised by text message.

I didn't ask him that either.

Without resolving anything, on Monday morning, we stepped back into our old working routine; he meets me outside my flat every morning, we walk to the tube and get a coffee together. We eat lunch and dinner together daily; sometimes, we get a takeaway if we're working late and, other times, we cook together.

Both of us ignore the huge elephant in the room.

The atmosphere between us is so intense; it's almost killing me. Our casual flirting has magnified tenfold and we can't seem to have a conversation without a sexual innuendo. There has been so much laughter. Things are going so well between us that it almost feels too good to be true. I'm afraid everything is going to fall apart again and we'll be back where we started.

All of our friends are now willing us to get together. Even James has taken it upon himself to try and set us up but I insist it's not what I want. I don't think he believes me, though.

I wouldn't believe me either.

Thursday quickly comes around and my nerves shoot through the roof but Jake is so confident this pitch will go well, that we'll win the account, that it calms me down.

"Just look at the work we've put in," he'd said last night as we poured through the pitch one last time over dinner. "Look how amazing everything is now that it has come together because we've collaborated. And it's not just us, Jude will be there and Lou."

We've never had a campaign where we've worked together the whole way from planning to creative execution. I know that, if Dad had let me do it myself like I wanted to in the beginning, it would never have turned out as good as this because Jake and I make each other work better.

"We're going to win this pitch. I'm sure of it, Maggs. Even if we don't, that's fine, too, because look at what we've learnt. Look at what we can do. Together."

I tell Jake to meet me at the office today instead of at my flat as I had to pick something up on my way in. He's already there when I arrive. Sasha gives me a strange, swoony look as I greet her outside of our office and Thomas rolls his eyes at her with a sarcastic sigh.

"Is something wrong?" I ask.

"I think you should go into your office," she says with a weird grin.

I do as she says and, as soon as I spot Jake, my draw drops. He's wearing a perfectly tailored three-piece suit. Dark navy, almost black with a crisp, white shirt and a navy, silk tie.

I'm momentarily lost for words and I think I'm sweating a little bit. He meets my eyes with a smile and my knees actually tremble. If I weren't already crushing so hard on him, I can guarantee this would have done it.

"Like what you see, Maggs?" he says just as he did last time he rendered me speechless with his appearance. It feels like a lifetime ago, now, that I saw him standing outside of St Paul's tube station.

Shit. I have to use words.

"We are definitely going to win this account when you turn up to pitch like that," he says, waving his hand to indicate towards my burgundy, peplum dress.

"Hopefully Mrs Stephenson doesn't try and take a bite out of you," I reply with a cheeky smile.

I watch him while he fixes his tie in the small mirror by my desk.

"You know, Maggs, we make a really good-looking couple," he says, catching me off guard as he meets my eye in the mirror.

"If you two are quite finished, our car is downstairs," Jude says from the door, making us both jump as Lou snickers behind him.

"We'll follow you down in a minute."

Jake looks at me quizzically.

"Before we go, I bought you something - Well, I bought *us* something." I pull out the small gift bag from under my desk and hand it to him. "I've had the best time working with you these past six weeks and just wanted to say thank you for not being a complete shithead."

He opens the gift box to find the sleek Mont Blanc pen with his name engraved in silver.

"I got a matching one, too. We match," I say lamely as Jake stares down at the personalised pen in his hand.

"This is amazing! Thank you," he says, coming to place a kiss on my forehead.

"It's blue ink. I know you like blue ink," I point out, not knowing where else to go with this. Smooth. Way to go, Maggie. He probably thinks you're a moron, now.

"I feel terrible. I didn't get you anything."

"You've given me more than you know," I answer honestly, thinking about the past 6 weeks and how much I've changed.

I'm not the miserable workaholic who avoided her friends and most social gatherings. I'm not as angry at life as I was or as highly strung.

I'm also not quite the old me, the girl I was before the accident and that's fine by me because I'm older now. I have different priorities like my family, friends and Jake.

"I'm a little nervous," I admit.

"Me, too," he says, taking my hand in his. Could he see that my fingers had begun to twitch? "I'll be right there with you, if you need me, which you won't because you know this thing back to front. Come on, let's go."

He pockets his new pen with an excited grin and picks up the equipment.

Off we go to complete the biggest pitch of our careers.

***

I couldn't have asked for a better presenting partner for the pitch. Between Jake and I, we answered all the questions quickly and clearly. Lou and Jude gave a great explanation of the different communication channels we would plan to use and our audience seemed to respond well to our campaign ideas. They even said that they really appreciated the time we took in creating mock-ups of the actual adverts when no other agency they had met with had thought to do that in advance.

I felt optimistic when we walked out of their Southwark office. Then, later that morning, they called us and said we are one of the final two agencies that they are considering.

I very much tried to ignore that today is Friday and that means Valentine's Day but everyone in the office was talking about it, making it hard to avoid.

My suspicions of Thomas and Sasha were confirmed when he walked in with a lovely bouquet of roses for her and promptly swept her up in a passionate kiss in front of the entire office. It was all very romantic.

"I should have thought ahead; all I got you was a pile of paperwork," Jake says, placing papers down neatly on my desk as he nods to the happy couple.

I really wanted to avoid the topic of Valentine's so I wouldn't have to talk about my plans. I know Laura has told him about the date she's arranged for me through that app and, if Jake wanted to say something about it, he did an excellent job of hiding it. Part of me wanted him to tell me not to go on the date. If he had, I would have cancelled in a heartbeat.

But he didn't.

So, I got myself dressed up and begrudgingly head out on my Valentine's date. All I know about the man is his name (Joe) and a brief description.

The night isn't off to a great start when I look up at the sign above the door to the pub. I double and triple check I'm at the right place. The pub is in a state of disrepair with shutters hanging off and paint which looked like it hadn't been touched for at least 50 years. Not the place you'd normally take a first date but I try not to judge from the outside. Maybe it's better on the inside?

"Maggie?" he asks in his thick, cockney accent as he approaches me.

"Joe?" I ask, panic building in my chest as I take in the man in front of me.

Surely Laura would have seen a photo of this man before setting me up? And I'm sure he is a lovely man but, from the few thing's she's told me about him, maybe his profile photo was from a time where he was 6 stone lighter and at least 15 years younger?

'He's 32, 6ft, black hair, designer stubble: Definitely your type,' she'd said with a wink as she basically described Jake.

"That's me name, don't wear it out," I fake a laugh while wondering if it's too late to run away.

"Come on, love. Let's get a drink, eh?"

He pushes the door open to the pub and the scent of stale beer and decades of old cigarette smoke soaked into the carpet hits me in the face. It's all I can do not to vomit on Joe's balding head which is at least half a foot shorter than me: Obviously, he's not

6ft.

I offer a hesitant smile as he greets multiple people while he walks through the dank, dimly lit room, leading me to a small, sticky table. I mentally thank myself for always having hand sanitiser in my handbag.

"Drink?" he asks.

"Rosé, please." He heads to the bar which has been dressed in tacky, foil hearts and pink, paper chain streamers.

I pull out my phone and begin to furiously type.

Maggie: WHAT THE HELL, LAURA?!

Maggie: FFS why did I let you do this?

Maggie: My date is an overweight, 55-year-old, balding gentleman.

James: Only Maggie would politely insult someone by adding gentleman.

Laura replies quickly, sending a photo of a handsome man with thick, black hair.

Laura: Is this him?

Maggie: Maybe 20 years ago.

Laura: Do you need an out? I can call with an emergency.

Maggie: No, you enjoy your date. I'm going out the bathroom window in 15 minutes.

Joe is stood at the bar with our drinks for what seems like a lifetime. He doesn't look like he is coming back any time soon either. He is talking to a tall, butch-looking woman. I give my best smile when they look my way although, for some reason, the woman just scowls at me like a British Bulldog chewing on a wasp.

Unable to take her scowl any longer, I drag my eyes from her to look around the rest of the room to get my bearings and suddenly feel extremely overdressed in my leather-look mini skirt, black jumper and chunky ankle boots. Everyone else looks comfortable, shall we say? - in their knockoff 'Jucky Couture' tracksuits that they, more than likely, bought from a dodgy-looking market stall in the Canary Islands ten years ago. One woman even looks like she's here in her pyjamas.

'Don't judge a book by its cover,' I scold myself for the third time this evening.

Joe eventually makes his way back and hands me my drink as I carefully try not to make eye contact with other customers who aren't trying to hide their glares.

I have never been more uncomfortable in all my life.

"That's me ex-wife. She owns the gaff," he says, pointing his thumb behind him. Delightful - that explains why she clearly doesn't like the look of me.

I take a sip of my wine and the taste of vinegar makes me feel sick. I'm glad I hadn't taken my jacket or scarf off yet as I eventually spot the sign for the loo.

"I'm actually going to pop to the bathroom. Please, excuse me."

I turn back around and see Joe chatting to some men at another table. Obviously, he won't miss me.

The toilets are hidden down a long corridor which is impossibly darker than the rest of the place due to the two missing lights hanging from the ceiling. There are three old, wooden doors; the ladies', the gent's and an alarmed fire exit at the very end of the corridor. I push through the door to the ladies' room with my bum so as not to touch anything. I'm passed the point of caring about being judgemental.

There's only one thing for it now. I get my bearings and look up at the small window at the back of the toilet cubicle. It's an old-style toilet with the cistern hanging on the wall about six feet off the ground and, even if I could reach the high window, it had long been painted shut.

Who paints a window closed? Talk about a fire hazard.

It's probably for the best, anyway. The window is at least eight feet from the floor and I have zero climbing ability. I would probably break both ankles on the landing and end up having to call Joe in the pub for help. That would not be ideal.

I pull out my phone in a blind panic and message the group chat. I'm surprised when I get a message back almost immediately.

Maggie: I'm in the loo's and the window is painted shut.

What do I do?

Jake: Fire exit.

I don't question how he knew that was a possibility as I open the door into the corridor, letting another woman past with a smile. She hisses at me

I read the big, red warning sign on the door. I weigh up my options as I stare at the notice informing me that an alarm will sound if the door is opened and I will be fined if it's not an emergency.

It's this or go back into the bar and confront my date.

I'm not proud of it but I can't face going back out there where I'm obviously not welcome and I don't have the courage to tell Joe to his face that this whole thing was a catastrophe. So, I do what any sane person would do. I push down on the cold, metal bar and heave the heavy door open.

The alarm screams in my ears but I don't hesitate. I run out of the building into the alley way behind the pub, the door slamming behind me. I fall straight into the strong arms of a familiar handsome man wearing perfectly-fitted jeans, his signature wool coat and a mischievous grin.

***

"Jake?!" I exclaim with so much undiluted delight that it shocks me a little bit.

"Ready to run?" he laughs, grabbing my hand pulling me away from that horrible pub and the alarm that is deafening the entire East End.

We don't stop running until we reach the closest tube station.

I thought I had an okay level of fitness since I try to keep on top of yoga but, after that small jog, it's painfully obvious that I am extremely unfit!

"Just give me a sec," I say as I'm doubled over, desperately trying to catch my breath. Note to self: Join a gym or a park run or something because this is embarrassing.

"Well, that was exciting," he says, grinning and straightening up my scarf. He brushes down my hair which, for most of the run, was billowing behind me in a tangled mess.

"Let's just get on the next train. I never want to come back here ever again," I say as I try to walk on wobbly legs and he tries his best not to laugh at me.

We jump on the DLR to head back to the city and we sit together in silence. I can tell he wants to say something but I'm sort of grateful he's holding it in. I already feel pathetic enough without him reminding me.

I risk a glance at him and I suddenly start laughing and I can't seem to stop. The absurdity of what happened hits me and it's hilarious. He joins in, laughing with me just as hysterically, making all our fellow passengers stare at us. We don't stop until we get off the tube again, our stomachs aching.

"Thank you for rescuing me. I'm sorry for ruining your Valentine's Day, I'm sure you had big plans."

"It must have been some date for you to attempt the window," he smirks, holding in a laugh this time, knowing we'll just start all over again.

"Ugh, honestly, it was awful. I can still smell the place on me," I say, liberally applying hand sanitiser. "Yet another bad date to add to the pile."

He leans over and sniffs me. "Ah, stale beer and pork scratchings mixed with Gucci perfume and Love Heart Carex hand gel."

I revel in the fact he remembers something as simple as the perfume I wear. The perfume I bought in Harrods when he took me out for our first dinner together. It feels like a lifetime ago, now.

"Why are you putting yourself through this, Maggs? You don't have to do it to please everyone else."

I want to say I'm doing it to get his attention but I don't. Instead, I give him a fraction of the truth.

"I know it's stupid but, since I started doing this dating thing, I've felt different. Like, I don't know. Somehow it's helping me remember who I was before I was 'a widow'," I say in air quotes. "I know it's stupid but I don't want to go back to being that girl. She was heartbroken and miserable and barely had any friends left. I know I'll never get over losing Philip but it felt good to live a little again. Maybe it wasn't the dates, after all. Maybe it was just saying 'yes' to doing more things with my friends and spending less time locked away with only my thoughts."

He thinks about what I've said in silence before looking at his watch.

"Right. It's only 8 o-clock and your recent experience of dating is dating idiots. Let me take you out, show you what a real date is."

"Sam wasn't an idiot but I get what you mean. It's Valentine's Day, though. We're never going to find anywhere and you've never been on a date; how do you know what makes a good one?"

"Because I've had a lot of time to think about what my perfect date would be and I know it's more your kind of thing than creepy, 'old man' pubs. Just trust me and don't judge until you see the end product."

I agree and we eventually get off our final tube at London Bridge. Jake leads us down the street, towards our office.

"Our office?" I ask as we walk into the large, sterile lobby. Hardly the epitome of romance.

"What did I say about judging? I'm just picking something up," he playfully tells me off.

When we get to our office, he disappears under his desk.

"I bought this to celebrate winning the pitch but I can always get us another one," he says, pulling up a bottle of Veuve Clicquot champagne. Next stop is the kitchen where he picks out two of the least tea-stained mugs he can find. Lastly, he finds a couple of branded beach towels from a campaign we ran a couple of years ago.

"Ready?" he asks, bundling everything into the backpack he found in our stash of left-over marketing products.

"Let me freshen up, first."

"Don't try to climb out of that window. It's a long way down," he says, smirking which I can't help but return with a slightly embarrassed laugh.

I look in the bathroom mirror and I'm not completely horrified by what I see. I quickly run my brush through my hair, removing all evidence of our impromptu marathon and swipe on more lip gloss. A quick spray of deodorant, a spritz of perfume and I'm good to go. Not perfect but he's seen me with a raging hangover so it's useless trying to be perfect when he knows I am far from it.

One last look in the mirror and I walk out of the bathroom to see him leaning casually on the wall next to the lift.

He looks like he's just stepped out of an issue of GQ. I really need to remember that he's doing this because he pities me and I really shouldn't think of him in a way that's more than friendly.

Hell, it's too late for that. My thoughts have already progressed from innocent crush to explicitly indecent.

It's hard to rein in my thoughts, especially when he combs his hair back away from his face with his fingers and looks up at me with his beautiful, blue eyes below his thick, black lashes.

"I just took a really exciting phone call," he says with a grin. "We got it. We won Stephenson's!"

"Are you serious?" I say, skipping into his embrace. I wrap my arms around his neck when he picks me up and twirls me around to celebrate.

He places me gently onto my feet but we stay in our embrace.

"We did it, Maggs! I knew we could," he says to me in his deep voice.

I step back before I melt into a complete puddle. I have got to pull myself together.

"Let's celebrate." He holds out his arm for me and leads me along the riverside of London Bridge City, towards the pop-up food market set up in front of Potters Fields Park. The delicious smell of bratwurst, gyros and fresh donuts waft through the air, making my tummy rumble.

What is it about the smell of food that makes you suddenly ravenous?

It's an unseasonably mild night which adds to the romantic atmosphere. Couples are walking hand in hand, taking in the beautiful city lights, stopping every so often to take photos of the breath-taking views on the other side of the Thames. The skyscrapers in the city are all glowing, the tower of London bathed in golden light and Tower Bridge stealing the spotlight with her beauty.

After we collect our food from the vendors, we find a spot

on a step with a beautiful view and lay out the towels so we can unpack the food. Jake had the idea of picking one thing from each food stall since we usually argue about what to order and, now that it's all spread out in front of us, it looks like it could feed an army, never mind just the two of us.

We've got pizza, gyros, paella and one of those spiral potatoes on a stick among other random dishes that Jake has assured me I'll like.

He pops the cork and pours champagne into our Sixth Street Advertising mugs before pulling me in for a selfie.

"For Instagram. Jude will be pleased with it. Plus, you look beautiful, as usual," he says, explaining the photo as he types something on his phone and making me blush in the same breath.

"Happy Valentine's Day," he says as he raises his glass to cheers again.

"Happy Valentine's Day, Jake," I reply, touching my mug to his, unable to control the butterflies making a mess of my stomach. "It's certainly one to remember. I'm sorry you got swept up in my drama."

"It's kind of selfish but I'm glad your date was shit. I'd much rather be here with you than sitting on my own, watching Netflix all night."

"Come on. You're trying to tell me that you had no Valentine's plans? No hot date?"

"Just what I told you. Netflix. On my own. I spend every Valentine's Day alone, I always have." It surprises me that someone like Jake, someone who craves company of any kind, would want to spend this day alone. "I thought about getting a pet but realised it's an awful idea."

"Me, too. The Valentine's Day thing, not the pet thing. I just thought that, this year, I would give it a go and look what happened."

"Well, like I said, I'm glad your date was shit. I would never have had the guts to ask you myself."

Jake and I always have fun whenever we hang out but, tonight, it feels so like much more. Something is different, something between us has changed. Maybe it's because we've both changed somewhat since we started working together: We are more comfortable in each other's company, plus the atmosphere down by the river is very relaxed and romantic.

We've eaten so much so we lie down to watch the stars with full stomachs and a warm sensation brought on by the champagne.

"You're a woman with a plan, where do you see yourself in five years?" he asks me randomly as his fingers wind through mine and our hands rest on the floor between us.

"Working with you, I hope," I say honestly, turning my head to look at him.

"Other than work," he prompts, leaning on his side to look at me.

"I don't know. Last time I had a five-year plan, everything was ticked off. Uni, job, husband. Things didn't go so well, though, so I stopped planning." I lean up and face him too. "Do you have a five-year plan?"

"I'm sure this will surprise you but yeah. Other than still working with you... I want to get married, have a couple of kids, move out of the city. Maybe closer to home."

"Jake Mills wants to get married and have kids?" I ask in disbelief. "Sorry, I just didn't imagine you'd ever want that."

"Yeah, I'm ready for a real relationship," he says, still holding my hand.

"I'm sure you'll find it."

I know that, as soon as Jake announces he wants a girlfriend, he'll have a mile long line of women behind him just waiting for their chance.

I just don't want to think about where that will leave me.

"If you ask me, this has turned out to be the greatest Valentine's Day I've ever had," he eventually says.

"You should have just asked me on a date in the first place then I could have avoided Mr Catfish in the East End." As soon as the words are out of my mouth, I regret saying it because this isn't a real date.

Now I feel like an idiot.

"Not that I think this is a date. Don't worry. I don't think this – Ugh, god. I'm going to stop talking. I'll get us some drinks," I say awkwardly as I get up to go to the bar stall before he can even process what I'm saying.

I really hate myself sometimes. Why do I have to say

stupid stuff?

I grab our fresh drinks, take a deep breath and hope to god that, by the time I get back to Jake, my cheeks have at least returned to their normal colour.

CHAPTER TWELVE

As the evening went on, the temperature dropped and (after a substantial amount of street drinking) we had the great idea to head to a bar on the Southbank. We dropped the bag back to the office, jumped on the tube to Waterloo and, after a couple of more drinks, Jake is slowly wearing me down on the idea of karaoke.

"Come on, Maggs," Jake pleads with me. "That was the deal. I won pool, you have to sing. Everyone is so drunk, they won't notice how bad we are. Plus, most of these people are tourists, they won't remember us when they return to their normal lives on Monday."

I answer with a groan.

"Jason Donovan and Kylie Minogue? Elton John and Kiki Dee?" he asks "No, *'Summer Lovin'*? I know you love the song and I know you know the words and it's a crowd pleaser."

He looks at me with a sparkle in his eye and my last remaining resolve melts away.

"Ugh, fine. Sign us up before I change my mind."

"I promise you'll enjoy yourself and, you said so yourself, you want to try new things. Just, this doesn't include dating a bunch of weirdos, just singing a song terribly off key with me."

Why does he make it sound so appealing?

He hands our request paper over to the boy running the karaoke (who can't be any older than 18) who informs us we're the next but one. Enough time to sink a glass of wine and maybe a sambuca shot for a bit of Dutch courage. I used to sing karaoke all the time - Philip loved it - so why am I terrified to get on that stage?

Jake orders our drinks and we cheers our shots: Down the hatch, it goes. The liquid warms my throat as the aniseed assaults my senses. I smile as Jake screws up his face.

"I don't know how that doesn't make you want to throw up," he says, wincing at the taste. "I am not having any more of those!"

The announcer calls our name from the stage so I quickly chug down my wine. This time, it's me who winces and tries not to vomit.

"Come on, Sandy," Jake says, grabbing my hand and lacing his fingers through mine, pulling me onto the stage as the boy hands me my microphone. It's too late to back out and, as the music starts, we start to sing.

Unsurprisingly, it's extremely fun. Once I get into it, that is. Jake was right, everyone is so drunk that they think we're the Beyoncé and Jay-Z of the Southbank and I don't hate it which, for an introvert like me, is a strange phenomenon. We dance together to the rhythm of the cheesy music as the crowd cheer and sing along. Jake is loving the attention (as usual) but doesn't pay any attention to it, even the older lady in the front row who is undressing him with her eyes. I'm not even mad; I know how she feels. It's hard to tear my eyes away from him.

As we reach the end of the song, Jake spins me out, ready for the big finale. Suddenly, I can't feel the stage below my feet anymore and I fall to my extremely embarrassing death.

Okay, yes, that may be over dramatic but the searing pain in my right foot is certainly no joke.

"Shit, Maggie," Jake says as he jumps down to the floor next to me as I try my hardest not to cry. "I'm so sorry. Are you okay?"

I don't speak for fear of bursting into tears. Instead, I settle for a shake of the head while pointing at my throbbing foot.

"Maggs? Can you stand?" he asks, looking an equal mix of concerned and guilty as hell as I shake my head once more.

I want the ground to swallow me whole. I'm so embarrassed that I almost don't hear the sounds of concern and smothered laughter from everyone that witnessed it. Almost.

"You can take her over there," the boy says, trying not to laugh in my face.

Christ. Why me?

Jake being the handsome knight in shining armour picks me up off the floor - bridal style - and takes me to an empty table next to the front door.

"Can we get another drink for the lady, please?" he asks as the boy saunters back to the bar with zero urgency or compassion for my now twice-it's-normal-size foot. "For the pain," he adds for my benefit.

He's staring at me with his beautiful blue eyes and I do momentarily forget the pain as my mind moves to the butterflies in my stomach. I also mentally thank the pedicure gods that I had my toenails painted as he takes off my boot to look at my foot.

"Maggs, can you say something. Please?"

"I'm just really trying not to burst into tears, right now." And it's becoming harder and harder as the embarrassment really sets in.

"We were really good up there. Did you at least enjoy yourself?" he says, trying to cheer me up.

"I was enjoying myself until you threw me off the stage," I reply through a fit of laughter. "I can't believe you did that, who does that?!"

"I'm so sorry," he says, laughing as though he's been holding it in. "No, honestly, I am. Nervous laughter. It's a curse"

The boy drops off my drink and I don't hesitate to throw it back and hand him back the empty shot glass.

"Come on, we'll get a taxi and take you to A&E," he says, pulling me up with one hand and holding my shoe in the other.

"That's not necessary. It's fine, really." I refuse to waste anyone's time over a stupid karaoke injury. "On second thoughts, A&E sounds great," I quickly add as pain shoots up my leg when I try to bear weight on my poor foot.

He scoops me up in his arms again and carries me out of

the bar. I am utterly mortified. That's it, we can never return. I'll have to move to Lithuania where no-one knows me.

I'm enjoying having Jake carry me in a Whitney-and-her-Bodyguard kind of way. All I need is for Jake to realise he *is* madly in love with me and snog me to within an inch of my life. Unlike The Bodyguard, we live happily ever after in my imagination.

Oh, shut up, Maggie. That's the shots talking.

***

It's a long and painful wait to be seen by a nurse in A&E who takes my blood and vitals. 5 hours to be exact. 2 hours after that, the sun is coming up and I finally get an X-ray before being called in to see a doctor.

I sobered up halfway through my wait in the waiting room and so they gave me the good painkillers. Now, I'm exhausted. Maybe I'm still a little bit drunk and definitely high on morphine.

"It's just a fracture, no break. This is the crack in the bone," the doctor says, pointing at the X-ray as I squint and try to make out the weird shapes. Has anyone really thought about how weird bones are? "Should take a few weeks to heal. The nurse will get you a boot to wear so you can walk. For the next few days, I would suggest keeping your weight off as much as possible."

Christ, those pain killers are good stuff. I can barely feel my face, never mind my broken foot. I'm slightly concerned that the doctor sounds like he's underwater but, at the same time, I'm not concerned at all. I feel great.

I wonder if the doctor knows he has green eyes.

"I got it," I say, not entirely sure what it is that I've 'got'.

"I'll get you a script for some codeine, too, for the pain," he adds to me. "But don't take it for another few hours. Have some sleep first and, when you wake up, you can take it."

"Ugh, pain. Do you know what really hurts, Doctor? Pluto."

"Erm, what do you mean, Miss Jones?" he asks, confused.

"Pluto must be in so much pain. Imagine spending your entire life thinking you're a planet and then, one day, some jobsworth at the International Astronomical Union decides you're not. It's just rude. Pluto must be so sad," I say, ending on a sob as real tears fall down my face. "And then, what about us? The people who were raised in the nineties, a time where you would say 'My Very Easy Method Just Speeds Up Naming Planets'. Now, what am I supposed to do to remember what order they are in? 'My Very Easy Method Just Speeds Up Naming'. Naming what? It's ridiculous. Without the P for Pluto, it just doesn't make sense. It's. Rude!" I say, completing my rant.

The poor doctor is barely containing his laugh. Jake doesn't even try to hide his as he gently wipes away my tears with his jumper sleeve.

"It's plain rude. My grandma would tell me to write a letter." I annunciate for emphasis before promptly bursting into more tears. "Jake, give me your phone. I want to tweet Neil deGrasse Tyson."

"I know, it's extremely rude. We can talk about it when we get home, okay? But I can't let you use my Twitter to start beef with Neil deGrasse Tyson," Jake says as he cradles my distraught face against his chest, dabbing my eyes while simultaneously apologising to the doctor for this seemingly random outburst. "I am impressed you could say International Astronomical Union perfectly, though," he adds softly.

"Well, Miss Jones," the doctor says, clearing his throat from the laughter he is holding in. "Once the nurse brings you your boot, your boyfriend can take you home."

"He's not my boyfriend. He's my best friend, business partner, long standing pain in the arse. But he has a beautiful face and a smile that makes me go weak at the knees so I keep him around." I attempt to wink at Jake but my eyes don't cooperate and just close for a few seconds. "Don't tell him I said this, doctor, but I have the biggest crush on him. It's his eyes, his beautiful, blue eyes. He just has to look at me and the world is a better place. And he's really kind, too. It's a shame he's way out of my league," I whisper loudly to the doctor as my eyes finally lose the battle and close completely.

"We can talk about that when we get home, too. And I think we'll go easy on the pain killers from now on. Right, Maggs?" I can hear Jake say as he softly kisses the top of my head and strokes my hair until I slowly fade into unconsciousness.

***

The next thing I'm aware of is my head banging against the door frame as Jake opens the door to my flat. Did I give him the key or did he take it out of my bag?

I don't care.

"Ow."

"Shit, sorry."

"S'okay," I mumble, my eyes still tightly closed.

He's much more careful as he manoeuvres through the sitting room towards the bedroom door. When he places me down on the bed that smells just like him, I suddenly realise this is not my flat. It's his.

"You brought me to your flat?" I ask as I groggily open one of my eyes. The bright light is blinding.

"Yeah, I thought it was easier to bring you here since I had my key and I know where everything is. Let me get you a T-shirt to wear and you can make yourself comfortable," he adds, turning off the big light and leaving the light on in the hallway until my eyes adjust.

I look to my side for the zip on my skirt through one squinted eye, the other still firmly closed.

"Help me, please," I whimper after a few attempts before realising the zip is at the back.

The bed shifts as he sits down in front of me and brushes my hair out of my face. Just that one moment of contact results in goosebumps pricking over every inch of my body. He reaches around to slowly lower the zip on the back of my skirt as I drink in the sheer pleasure of his touch. Yes, I take this opportunity to inhale him like any other red-blooded woman would.

It's a crazy thought but I wish this were real. I wish he were undressing me for a different reason.

He starts to move off the bed when my arm gets stuck trying to pull my jumper over my head.

"You're going to have to help me get it off. And help me stand so I can get my skirt off."

He lets out a throaty laugh and I wonder how hilarious this looks to him.

He's a man with a reputation. Surely, he's helped a woman get undressed before. So why does he look so unsure?

He's gentle as he untangles my arm from my sleeve and easily pulls my jumper over my head. His fingers graze my side and my body responds with an embarrassing shiver and accompanying goose bumps.

His warm hand lingers for a moment on my bare skin, noticing my reaction for the first time, his Adam's apple bobbing slightly like he's trying not to react himself.

"Thank you," I say, barely above a whisper but not caring that I'm sat in front of Jake Mills in nothing but my unzipped skirt, a lacy bra which leaves nothing to the imagination and an attractive medical boot.

He clears his throat and pulls his T-shirt on over my head

while I shove my arms through the holes. He then helps me to stand on one foot so I can wiggle out of my skirt.

"I've never put clothes *on* a woman before so this is all new for me." He laughs nervously.

"I meant thank you for everything. For always being there when I needed you on those shitty dates; for standing up for me when Cylvie was being a bitch; for making an effort to prove to me that we can work together and for showing me new things. For being my partner. You're one of the most important people in my life and I don't know how I managed to live so long without you, I'm scared that, one day, you'll wake up and meet someone and you won't want to hang around with us anymore."

"I'm sorry I spent so many years being a twat. And you don't need to worry about me meeting someone. At this point, you're stuck with me. I don't think I could live without you anymore and I most definitely don't *want* to live without you but we'll talk about that tomorrow," he says sincerely.

I pull the bobble off my wrist and move to tie back my hair but, as my hands are busy trying to pull the uncooperative bundle together, I slowly start to tilt to the side. Jake catches me by my waist before I face plant his bed and the contact shocks me again. He doesn't remove his hands once I'm upright. We just stare at each other, not in a weird kind of way but more like an I-can't-bear-to-take-my-eyes-off-you kind of way.

"I really enjoyed our date tonight, even if I did maim you and I hope you did, too. I wish I had plucked up the courage and asked you out sooner, could have avoided those crappy dates you went on," he says, leaving me wondering if I had imagined what he'd said. It's something he'd say in my dreams.

Was tonight a real date? Is that what he said or was that a painkiller-induced hallucination?

He's sat next to me, now, with one leg tucked under himself and the other stretched out behind me, his chest almost touching my side. I hadn't realised that my hand was resting on his thigh or that he was tracing patterns on the back of my neck with his fingertips until another shiver runs down my spine.

"Jake?" Again, I'm hypnotised when he looks at me. "Will you kiss me?"

"I think it's time to get some sleep," he says, letting me down gently.

Oh, god. Did that just happen?

"Ugh, yeah, it was stupid. I blame your eyes. Your stupid, beautiful eyes."

"I want to, believe me, I really want to kiss you. It's taking all my self-control not to but I don't want our first kiss to be one you don't remember when you wake up. Plus, you're pretty high on morphine; it wouldn't be right for me to take advantage."

My brain is too foggy to fully process his words. It sounded like he said he wants to kiss me.

"Please, don't leave me alone tonight. Sleep here with me?"

"I'd love to," he says softly. "Let me get changed."

He helps me lay back, tucks the quilt around me and, as soon as my head hits the pillow that smells just like him, my eyes refuse to stay open any longer. The next thing I know is feeling his warm arms wrap around me and his lips press to the side of my neck as I sigh and relax into his embrace, my body melting into his as he holds me tight.

I've spent so long trying to stop myself falling for Jake that I hadn't realised I already had. What was an innocent crush feels like so much more and I'm scared that I'll not be able to go back if things go wrong.

My worries are long forgotten when I feel him pulling me in close as he buries his face into my neck again. He kisses me gently along my shoulder before I feel his head settle onto the pillow next to mine

"Goodnight, Maggie," is the last thing I hear before I give in to unconsciousness.

***

I wake up to bright sunshine streaming in through the large, familiar window. Sitting up to take a better look around, I'm greeted with a sharp pain in my foot.

Right, my fractured foot.

My brain is foggy as I look around the room and struggle to put everything together in my mind. The bed is soft and comfortable, the dark quilt still wrapped around me. I feel safe and warm.

Hang on, what am I wearing? Did I get changed? I can't read the writing upside-down but I think its Jake's crazy golf T-shirt.

All at once, my memories return although they're still a little blurry.

Oh, god. Jake.

Oh, I'm so stupid. Why did I ask him to kiss me? Obviously, he was going to reject me. I look around the floor but can't seem to locate my stupid boot or crutches.

Memories of him undressing me. Oh, sweet Jesus. At least I had on a nice bra and a decent pair of knickers that was halfway between slutty and classy. They didn't match or anything - I wasn't that put together - but at least they weren't grey.

Thank god Laura had added a bikini wax and pedicure to our appointment last week; the alternative would have been mortifying.

This... Well, this is just extremely embarrassing.

I stand and try to hop to the door to find Jake so I can apologise for being an embarrassment but, instead, I wobble and catch myself on the floor in some sort of downward dog yoga pose with a thud and a squeal.

Ow. That hurt like hell.

"Shit, Maggs. Are you okay? You should have shouted," he says as he runs into his bedroom to help pick me up off the floor. Again. He sits me on the end of the bed, looking relieved that (at least, this time) he wasn't responsible for my fall.

"Yeah, I'm fine... Just want to find my boot. I should really ring a taxi and go die of embarrassment at home," I say, not meeting his eyes. "What time is it?"

"It's just after 2 pm. Don't go just yet. I made you some breakfast. Well, lunch. Waffles and pancakes. I was about to come and wake you up," he says as he bends down with my boot to put it on me and handing me two crutches.

"Oh, right. Thanks," I say, not knowing what else to say but feeling extremely nervous and embarrassed in equal measure.

"Do you, uh... Remember much? From last night? I honestly don't think I've seen anyone get so high from such a small dose of morphine." He grins, teasing me as he shoves his hands in his jean's pockets. I want nothing more to return his grin and forget about everything but I just keep replaying the moment I begged him to kiss me in my head and the moment he politely said 'no'.

Stupid.

"Sadly for my ego, I remember most of it. It was the morphine talking so don't feel guilty about your rejection. Obviously, it was crazy that you and I would - You know..." I say, trying to dismiss the fact that I was deadly serious when I asked him to kiss me. The last thing we need is awkwardness.

"Oh... Right," he says, echoing my earlier statement. "Well, come and get some food. You must be starved. You haven't eaten since our food last night."

"In fairness, we probably ate a week's worth of calories in one go. But yes, I'm starving," I reply.

"You want some help?" he asks.

"No, I should really get some practice using these things," I say as I struggle to coordinate my crutches and hopping.

I clumsily follow him out into the kitchen dining area and, when he sees me struggle, he guides me with his arm around my waist. There's that tingling sensation again.

"It might take some getting used to but we can practice today," he says when we reach his breakfast bar where he has stacks of pancakes and waffles surrounded by bowls of fresh fruit and a big jar of Nutella. He helps me take a seat on the high stool before taking a seat opposite me.

I'm painfully aware I only have his T-shirt and my knickers on. At least, the T-shirt covers most of my modesty.

"This is incredible. I knew you could cook, obviously, but I didn't know you could make pancakes and waffles like this. Don't let Laura know; she'll be out for blood."

"Mum taught me. She loves pancakes but, like you've said in the past, I'm a mummy's boy so who knows if they're actually good or not?"

"Yep, this is incredible," I say as I chew my way through a large bite of waffle, Nutella and strawberries. "Seriously. I could eat this all day every day and not get bored."

He laughs his throaty laugh and starts to load his own plate up.

"I owe you a massive apology and I should have said this weeks ago, it's at least a decade late. I judged you and I got it all wrong."

"You're surprised I'm not an arrogant, obnoxious womaniser?" he asks, grinning at me and repeating the words I threw in his face not long ago.

"Not anymore. I remembered the kind of man you were that first night and last night was perfect, aside from the broken foot. I'm just sorry I never took a moment to remember the man you *are*, instead of avoiding the man I thought you were for such a long time."

"It's not your fault, Maggie. If anyone should get the blame, it's me. I spent three years pushing you away then, when I realised what I'd lost, I acted like a twat to get your attention. I'm not saying that some of the stuff wasn't true but it was exaggerated and embellished whenever you were around. I don't think there were half as many women as I'd have you believe. I didn't know what else to do. After Philip died, you would only talk to me when you were pissed off at me or berating me over something so I kept it going. I didn't know how else to get you to talk to me again."

"You went on like that because you wanted to talk to me? Why didn't you just - I don't know - talk to me like a normal human being?" I laugh. "I missed you, the old you who used to sit and play on my brother's Xbox and eat all of Mum's posh biscuits. I missed the boy who would pick us up in his little, silver Saxo with his leather jacket and drive us around wherever we needed to go."

"I didn't know how to talk to you because you weren't the same person anymore either. You had grown up; you weren't the girl I pushed away. You were older and I was intimidated. You are easily the smartest and the kindest person I know; you're loyal, funny and you're drop dead gorgeous. Add them all together and I was nervous."

I can feel the blush warming my face like it has so many times with him.

"Well, I'm glad we're friends again. I'd never have gotten this cool boot if we weren't," I say, laughing again to ease the sexual tension that surrounds us.

"I'm really, really sorry for what happened to your foot. I'm hoping you'll let me make it up to you."

"You could start by driving me home? And then to my parents' house for James' birthday party? I know you don't normally come to those things and they're usually rubbish but I've got a feeling this time will be different. If you come, that is. Mum might even try her hand at pyrotechnics again."

"If you're sure you want me to come, I'll be there. I can't wait to see you explain that to your mum," he smirks, pointing at my boot.

"I'd be pretty scared, if I were you. If she finds out it was your fault that her darling daughter was maimed, she'll be calling for your head on a stake."

"Shit. Didn't think of that. I'll just use you as a human shield; it's not like you can move very fast," he says playfully.

"I suppose it is in my best interest to protect you. I'd very much like to keep you around. For professional purposes, obviously."

"Is that the only reason? Professional purposes?" he asks, cocking an eyebrow.

"I like having you around," I say, wary of my words. He is way too suggestive this morning and it's actually going to be the death of me.

CHAPTER THIRTEEN

After we'd finished our food and watched a little TV, Jake drove me home to get changed for James' party. I felt extremely lazy, driving two streets over but, at the same time, I couldn't face walking it with my crutches. I have terrible balance at the best of times, never mind hopping while simultaneously trying to use two metal poles to keep me upright. I'm glad I have Jake to hold on to me while I attempt to get used to them.

Showering was another challenge. Luckily, I have a walk-in shower and didn't need any help getting in. Jake lazed on my bed, watching TV and, when I was securely wrapped in my towel once more, he helped me back into my bedroom and sat me at my dressing table. My good leg was starting to ache from taking all my weight for most of the day.

I'm not sure how I'll manage overnight without him being here to help me move around. Maybe, if I have enough to drink, I'll have enough Dutch courage to ask him to stay with me without feeling desperate for his company.

I try to put the mortifying experience to the back of my mind while we are in close proximity in my small bedroom. Just me, Jake and the huge elephant squashed in here with us. I catch him looking at me a couple of times and he looks like he is about to say something. On more than one occasion, he thinks better of it and even excuses himself to get us a drink from the fridge to avoid my quizzical gaze.

Once I'm ready, he drives us to Mum and Dad's house in Kingston-upon-Thames. There has been a shift between us today and I know it's because of my stupid remarks last night. First, I make him think that I thought we were on a date and then I tried to get him to kiss me. God knows what else my morphine induced brain made me say to him.

***

"Jacob, dear, I wasn't expecting you. What a lovely surpr-," Mum cuts off, her face changing from delight at the sight of Jake's arm hugging me tightly to his side to absolute terror as she spots my foot. "Maggie, my sweet baby girl! What happened to you?" she cries out, running towards me and I brace myself for impact.

"Mum, it's fine, honestly," I say as she attempts to hug me but doesn't quite know where is best for her to stand.

"I'm afraid I swept your daughter off her feet," Jake says, raising his eyebrows at me in amusement at his own joke. "Get it?"

I roll my eyes at him with a smile, letting him know that he's funny but also being a knob.

"More like twirled me off my feet, resulting in my fall

from a three-foot-high stage."

Mum looks at Jake in horror. "I saw the video on The Facebook. Your brother took great delight in showing me when he got here but I didn't realise you were hurt. If I had known, I certainly wouldn't have laughed at it. You should have called me. I hate to think of you all alone in that flat, struggling."

"Mum, I was fine. I stayed with Jake. Anyway, it's just a fracture. Honestly, it looks worse than it is with the boot." She looks at me with a wide grin, then looks to Jake and back to me.

Should have kept my mouth shut.

"And I've told you a thousand times, it's Facebook not *The* Facebook. You don't need the 'the'… Hang on, what video on Facebook?"

Ignoring me, she indicates for Jake to usher me up the garden path and straight into the living room.

"Come on in, sweetheart, we'll find you a comfy seat." I roll my eyes to Jake as she walks in front of me, mumbling something about the dangers of karaoke and me finally 'seeing sense'. Not too sure what that's about but I'm sure she'll bring it up before the night is through.

As soon as we walk through the door, Mum's off, hunting for something in the storage seat below the bay window. I learnt a long time ago not to ask questions or poke the beast when she's like this. I just let it happen, smile and nod when required.

"Kev, come and see your poor daughter," Mum shouts through the house. Somehow, he heard her and wanders into the room. Dad hugs and kisses me before shaking Jake's hand, his gaze narrowing on the hand that is clutching onto me. Dad eyes him up with suspicion before following Mum into the other room. How much more embarrassment can I take?

I spoke too soon.

"Well, if it's not Sandy and Danny themselves. Nice accessories," my brother taunts me, pointing at my boot and crutch before turning to his best friend. "Didn't know you were coming, Jake? When I asked you a few weeks back, you said you'd rather stick pins in your eyes. Someone persuade you otherwise?"

"I may have a broken foot but that doesn't mean I can't give you a dead arm, James," I threaten.

"She'll have to catch me first," he says, pulling Jake in for a manly hug, back clap thing like they do. My brother knows me well and he jumps just out of my grasp at the last second before my knuckle had a chance to hit a nerve in his arm.

"What video is mum on about?" I ask my brother accusingly "Apparently, you know something I don't."

"It's all over the internet. I'm surprised you haven't seen it. You're viral, sis. Lad Bible, Uni Lad, even Buzzfeed have shared it."

He hands me his phone as I watch in horror. We look so happy, smiling and laughing, and we dance much closer than I remember. And then, it happens. I spin, I squeal and then thump. I hit the deck.

And it's on the internet for the world to see.

"Oh my god, did you know?" I glare at a guilty Jake.

"Yeah, it was up by the time we got to the hospital but I didn't want to tell you when you were high on morphine because, well, you were crying at every slight thing. You're scary as hell when you're mad and sober so I chickened out and hoped no-one would say anything," he says, looking to my brother for protection as if I wouldn't hurt the both of them.

"'Oh, people are drunk, they won't remember us'," I say in a mock impression of Jake. "You forgot about the bloody internet!"

"Look, you were great, everyone loved you. You even got a standing ovation."

"They were trying to get a better look at me on the bloody floor."

"Now, now, don't argue. You're only on day one. It's a bit early for your first lovers' tiff," my brother jokes. I don't have time to hurl any other insults at him as Mum comes back into the room so I settle for throwing one of mum's little scatter cushions at him instead.

"So, how long have you been sleeping with my daughter," Mum asks Jake as she pads the love seat with multiple cushions to prop me up.

Jake doesn't reply. Instead, he chokes on air, sending my brother into a fit of laughter.

"Mum!"

My brother just laughs harder.

"You can't just ask someone that. And nothing is going on between us. We're friends, like we have been for thirty years." If my face goes lobster red one more time today, I fear it'll stay that way.

"I can assure you, my intentions with your daughter are honourable," he says, laughing as he sits on the arm of the love seat with his arm draped around my shoulder. It's not helping our argument.

I don't bother telling him that he could sit on the love seat with me - there is room - although Mum would probably combust if he moved any closer.

"Can we talk about something else, please?"

"Don't be so immature, Maggie. There is no shame in sex. I was young once. Women have needs that need to be met and you've been alone for quite some time. No matter how old you are, nothing is better for stress. It'll keep you young, endorphins or something. Your father and I have been taking a class. 'Sex with someone you trust and care for releases endorphins. Endorphins are good'," she quotes as I die inside at the thought of my parents doing it at their age.

"A sex class? Yeah, I'm going to be sick," my brother says as he dry heaves.

"Oh, be quiet. It's done wonders for our marriage. Since you two have taken over the business, we've had so much more time together. Morning, noon, night - It doesn't matter. Just whenever the mood strikes."

Jake can't contain his laughter any longer as the colour drains from my face. Because that's what every family party needs, parents bragging about their sex life which is, evidently, more exciting than mine.

"You needn't laugh, Jacob; your mother is the one who introduced us to the class. She and I compare notes," Mum says, wiping that smirk off his face.

Jake removes his arm from me and stares at Mum with his mouth hanging open, his skin has a slightly green hue and I swear he's close to throwing up. I would feel sorry for him if I weren't completely mortified myself.

"I'm going to find the straight bleach. Excuse me, please," my brother says as he walks away from us, shaking his head as though he is trying to shake the conversation from his memory.

"Speaking of your parents, here they come, now," she says as she spots them coming up the garden path. "I'll let them in," she adds, running off to answer the door.

"Pretend this conversation never happened?" I plead.

"Deal."

"I know you said you'd drive us back but should I book us an Uber home later, instead?"

"Yep. Do that. If I have to endure stories of our parents' sex-capades all evening, I need to be drunk. I better go say 'hi' to Mum and Dad, too. Hopefully, I can look them in the eye. I'll bring drinks back with me."

"So, you and Jake, huh?" my brother asks me after he

passes Jake in the doorway with a raised eyebrow. "Singing cheesy romantic duets on the karaoke on Valentine's Day? Heard you spent the night there, too? Mum was just telling Angie and Margaret."

"What is with everyone? There is nothing going on. We're close friends. We run a successful ad agency together, partners. That's it. Can a male and female not be friends without something going on? Besides, *'Summer Lovin'* is a song about a girl who thinks she's in love and a guy who's desperate to shag her."

"Okay, you got me there. It is normal for men and women to be friends; I have a lot of female friends. But that man in there is in love with you and has been for a lot longer than I've known. Believe me when I say that I've known a long time. He's good at hiding it from you."

I don't say anything. Instead, I opt for a *pft* of disbelief.

"Why do you think he hated hearing you talk about dating? Or why he lost it when you were planning on sleeping with Sam? Plus, we talk about it all the time. Scratch that. *He,* literally does not stop talking about it and, if I'm honest, we're all sick of him not making a move and then feeling sorry for himself. I guess - by the look on your face - you really didn't know. If you don't feel the same, you need to tell him before you get his hopes up."

I don't know how to respond to James. Is it true? Does Jake have feelings for me? Why didn't he tell me before I went on those dates or, you know, last night when I embarrassed myself and asked him to kiss me. If he has feelings for me, why *didn't* he kiss me last night? I desperately try to remember what he said to me but my mind is foggy and I can't make sense of it all.

"You obviously have feelings for him, too, Maggie. I think you know you do and that's okay. I say this as your big brother; you deserve to be happy. You think I would have let him get this far with you if I didn't know that he's the right person to make you happy? The smile you had on your face when you walked through that door with him tonight - Hell, the smile you have whenever you're with him. Well, I've not seen that smile for over eight years and I'd like it to continue."

I know he's right. Spending time with Jake has pulled down walls that, until recently, I hadn't even realised I had built over the years. In such a small amount of time, he has become as necessary to me as breathing. I crave his company when he isn't around and relax the moment I see his smile light up his face.

I lost myself when Philip died. I had been with him my entire life and, without him, I didn't know who I was anymore. We shared a family, we shared friends and hobbies so, when he was taken from me, I had nothing to call my own. Nothing that didn't painfully remind me of what I had lost.

Although, at one point, we were all friends, this relationship I have now with Jake is my own. We have our own little moments together; we understand each other like no-one else has been able to. He makes me smile and laugh and not give a shit about what people think about me, something that was such a foreign concept to me a few weeks ago.

I had always known he was good looking. How could I not be physically attracted to him when he is every girl's fantasy? Besides that, he's kind, caring and considerate. He's funny and I can tell he has so much love to give. Ever since that first night at the pub, the day our dads threw us together in an unlikely partnership, he just needs to look in my general direction and my knees go weak.

I have to admit, there is a lot of chemistry between us. A lot of flirting and innuendos and, looking back on the times there's been just the two of us, there's been a lot of romance that I hadn't took any notice of. But there are reasons I shouldn't even entertain the thought of more than a friendship with him which is why asking him to kiss me last night was reckless. There's the company, for a start. What would happen if things ended badly between us? And what about our friendship? I've come to depend on him too much to lose him.

Jake joins us again, this time, coming to sit closer to me on the actual seat instead of the arm of my chair. He pulls me into his side, back to reality, and I can't help but lean in all too comfortably as my brother gives me his all-knowing look.

I know he's right. He knows he's right. I do have feelings for Jake Mills. I would go as far as saying I'm falling in love with him but can I see a future with him? I'm not sure.

Jake hands me a glass of wine filled to the brim. You know, like a real glass of wine that empties half a bottle; exactly what I needed after my lightning bolt realisation. The realisation of maybe it wasn't the fact that I was trying to put myself back on the market, maybe it was Jake who brought me back to life all along.

I shove all thoughts to the side when Jake asks me if I'm okay, sensing that I'm having some sort of epiphany.

I'm thankful when James steps in to redirect the conversation. "So, I was thinking we go mingle for a bit, say 'hello' to everyone we have to and, maybe, play a little Jones family bingo to keep ourselves entertained? Then, we sneak away from the grown-ups and down to the summer house like we did when we were teenagers."

"Sounds like a great idea," Helen says as she joins us. I didn't even realise she was here. "Thanks for leaving me back there, by the way, James. I just had to endure a conversation with everyone's Mums about a new Kama Sutra book they're reading in some sex class." She adds a dramatic shiver for affect.

"It's every man or woman for themselves tonight. Sorry, babe," he says, kissing her on the cheek.

"Don't touch me. She's just detailed her Love Honey order in depth and I feel like I need to gouge out my brain." We all dry heave at that thought. "Think I better kill a few braincells with booze," she adds, plucking my brother's bottle of Bud from his hand.

Thankfully, we turn our attention to other topics of conversation, including my karaoke accident. At least Helen gives me an ounce of sympathy and it's not long before Laura, Harry and

Simon arrive.

Once our drinks are replenished, we run through the rules for Jones family bingo. It's a game we played as kids to pass the time at Mum and Dad's parties. Although, this time, we are all in our 30s and playing with alcohol instead of chocolates.

When we were kids, we'd be hyped up on sugar, often keeping us awake until long after the party had finished. Now that we're respectable adults, it's a sure-fire way of getting completely rat arsed in the least amount of time possible - A godsend when the older lot are discovering how much they still love sex.

"So, it's a drinking game?" Simon asks.

"Yeah. So, take one drink every time someone asks when James and Helen are getting married," Laura says, typing into the notepad on her phone, knowing that's a topic that usually comes up at one of these things since they're both thirty-three and have been together for over a decade now.

"One drink every time someone asks if Maggie and Jake are shagging or suggests they should be shagging. Or even just going out with each other," Helen puts in and amending her suggestion slightly as I roll my eyes at her. Clearly, the rumours are spreading. "Whatever. If your names are mentioned in the same sentence, we drink."

"Can we not discuss the topic, quickly? I mean, they should be going on a date," Harry asks. We all drink.

"They did last night," James says. We all drink.

"Apparently, Jake needs to work on his dating skills,"

Laura snickers.

"First off, we had a lovely night until karaoke-gate. And, secondly, can we move on, please? We'll be drunk before the game starts at this rate," I beg

"Two drinks whenever someone brags about something new that they've bought or are planning on buying. Bonus drink if they mention how much it cost," Jake says, coming to my rescue and changing the subject.

"Two drinks when they brag about something a kid or grandkid has done," Harry continues.

"Down the whole drink when someone over the age of fifty mentions sex in any context," I finish the rules as we share a collective shiver.

"First one to tap out buys the rest dinner next weekend," James finishes, adding the wager. "I reckon that, if we speak to enough people in the next hour, annoy the hell out of them all, no-one will give a shit when we sneak off to the summer house."

We all agree and spread out to mingle with other guests. Jake makes sure to stick by my side after I insist that I can't actually move without his assistance. No-one fights me on my request even though any of them would be able to help me. I think they want to see where this goes as much as everyone else, me included.

I'm still not convinced that Jake sees me as anything more than his friend, no matter what my brother has to say about it. Jake isn't usually shy when it comes to women; he knows what he wants and has the confidence to go for it. It pains me to say but I've seen it in action. So, if he does share my feelings, why hasn't he told me about it himself?

"Here we go," Jake whispers in my ear as his parent's approach us. We hadn't even had chance to stand up so I feel slightly awkward when Margaret speaks as I am almost sat in her son's lap.

"Well, it's nice to see you two *together*," she says as she and Ray sit on the couch next to where we're sat. We drink at the suggestive tone she uses when she says the word 'together'. "How long has this romance been going on?"

Another drink.

"Mum," Jake says, warning her.

"You just make a great couple, that's all. And everyone is so happy to see you both together," she says, smiling as she uses that word again.

Another drink.

"Just don't mess it up, son," Raymond says sternly, bringing me back to Earth with a bang. If we messed it up, what would happen to the company he and my dad have spent their lives building?

The interrogations didn't end with Margaret and Ray. People were obviously excited about seeing Jake. Since he hasn't been to one of these parties in a long time, they wouldn't leave him alone. They wanted to know everything about his life in the last twelve years. My aunties and uncles, our parents' friends, even old neighbours. Everyone wants a piece of him and yeah, I was jealous because I wanted to keep him to myself.

I wanted to know if what James said was true. Has Jake had feelings for me for a long time? How long? What kind of feelings? Why hasn't he told me?

And, if he doesn't feel that way, why would James make it up? It has to be true, right?

I conclude that Laura has known for a while. It would explain why she's always the one to help James diffuse the tension between me and Jake like at the bar when we fought over the slight possibility that I would sleep with Sam. Instead of calming me down, she was right at the bar with James and Jake, talking him down. Clearly, she knew it had the possibility to blow up in my face.

There is no way Helen doesn't know; James would have told her in detail. They can't keep anything from each other. Helen even says that, if she can't tell James, she doesn't want to know.

If what James said is true, that he can't stop talking about it, that everyone is sick of him not making a move, why hasn't Harry told me before now?

As I stand here, smiling and nodding at Janice from next door as she coos over Jake, it dawns on me that he has never denied that we're together when we've been asked - it's always been me - and everyone we've spoken to tonight have asked us something along those lines. People asking how long we've been together and me denying that there's anything other than friendship between us. Even Philip's Mum and Dad gush about what a lovely couple we make and say we should have gotten together long ago.

Jake just smiled at them when they spoke about it, maybe out of politeness, maybe in agreement. Maybe he does think we should have gotten together a long time ago and I keep shoving him firmly back in the friend zone like a complete shithead whenever someone uses our names in the same sentence.

I'm the reason he hasn't said anything, I'm the one who insists we're just friends. No wonder he won't dare say anything to me, he probably thinks I'm going to reject him.

But he did tell me. I remember now. Right after he gently turned me down, he explained. I was just too high on painkillers or maybe too embarrassed to really hear what he was saying.

'I want to, believe me, I really want to kiss you. It's taking all my self-control not to but I don't want our first kiss to be one you don't remember when you wake up.'

I need to get him on his own. I need to talk to him and clear this whole thing up.

I honestly have no idea what to say or how to say it so, instead, I stand, half listening to the conversation he has with Janice and half overanalysing every single moment we've shared in the last six weeks.

CHAPTER FOURTEEN

Less than an hour after we start our drinking game, we were all well on our way to being pissed and have all been told off by my mum for being childish.

Thirty years old and still getting told off by my mum for getting drunk when, by the end of the night, you can guarantee she will be the drunkest one here.

So, to avoid a further telling off, we all settled down a little on the drinking and just made an effort to speak with Mum's party guests.

Jake has kept his arm wrapped around my waist as he stands behind me all evening, letting me lean against him, propping me up and taking half of my weight to give me some relief. People offer me seats but I decline, using the excuse that I will seize up if I sit for too long.

I'm still not confident on the crutches and the alcohol doesn't help my balance at the best of times so, if Jake is willing to keep his arms around me, I'll take full advantage of that. That's what I'm telling myself, anyway, that he's helping me balance and that's why I need him to hold me. It's totally not the fact that I crave his physical contact. No not at all.

It hasn't helped convince people that we're just friends either. That and the fact that everyone has seen the karaoke video on Facebook… And the photo of us that Jake took on our romantic champagne picnic by Tower Bridge that Jude posted on social media last night, wishing our followers a 'Happy Valentine's Day'.

I even stopped denying that we are together after a while. Jake hasn't denied it all evening and I decided that, by the end of tonight, I'm going to tell him exactly how I feel.

More and more of our conversation comes back to me as the night goes on. I remember what I said about him to the doctor in the hospital, how he said we'd talk about it when we got home but, clearly, I was in no fit state to do that.

I've spent the better part of the evening scrutinising our friendship and I suppose there are a lot of reasons to think we're a couple.

"Let's go to the summer house before the others make their way down. Your dad got the fire pit started earlier so it'll be nice and warm. I think he knew we would all hide down there, eventually. I could also do with five minutes to chill. I forgot how intense Jones family parties can be," Jake says, taking my drink so he can carry it for me. He helps me navigate through the kitchen and out of the back-patio doors. We pass my brother who winks at me as we quietly sneak out, avoiding all the 'grown ups'.

On the outside, I'm rolling my eyes at him. On the inside, my stomach has tied itself in knots, thinking about me and Jake, alone in the garden.

This is my chance to speak to him and I still have no idea what I'm going to say. I'm so nervous that I'm shaking and Jake notices.

"Are you cold?"

"I'll be okay when we get to the fire pit," I lie.

He leads me down the garden path, past the goldfish pond and wishing well water feature that Mum insisted on having custom built but now refuses to go anywhere near it out of fear of frogs.

Six weeks ago, I would have put money on Jake pushing me in the pond.

The summer house is a large shed at the bottom of the garden surrounded by lush, green trees and shrubbery that my dad turned into a garden bar 'before it was cool', as he likes to remind us. We would sneak out of family parties as teenagers to come down here and help ourselves to the vodka and gin he kept under the high bar.

Back then, there were a few collapsible garden chairs, a mesh table and a plastic storage box where the booze was kept. Now, there is a tall, wooden bar with a built-in beer pump and keg, hanging shelves containing top end spirits and cosy outdoor sofas with cushions and blankets. A hanging egg chair sits in the corner opposite big, double doors that open out onto a paved area where the fire pit sits.

I think our parents must have figured out what we were doing as kids because, over time, the spirits would change to cheap home brand and tasted like it was mixed with 90 percent water but we still loved feeling like rebellious kids.

It's been a long time since I've been in here. There are now shelves around the eves of the room, housing empty whiskey bottles from all over the world that Dad and his friends have finished. Rock'n'roll memorabilia he's hoarded from the 70s and 80s decorate the walls. He's even got one of those cardboard peanut and pork scratching hangers that his mate from the pub down the road got him for his birthday.

"Tonight has been great. I'm glad you invited me." I don't mention that James invited him weeks ago but he declined because of our fight.

"Why did you stop coming to our parties all those years ago?" I ask, curious.

"I don't know. I guess I just said 'no' to my parents enough times that they stopped asking me to come in the end."

"That doesn't answer my question. Why did you say 'no' in the first place?"

"Can I ask you something?" he asks me to avoid my question again, suddenly looking nervous.

"Sure."

"Last night, when you asked me to kiss you-"

"I had just about gotten over that embarrassment. Maybe I just read the room wrong?" I say in a question, hoping he'll tell me that I wasn't wrong at all.

"Answer me honestly. Did you want me to kiss you or was

it the morphine talking?"

"Jake..." I plead with him not to make me answer that question before I have chance to probe him a bit more about his feelings.

He just raises his eyebrows at me and I sigh in defeat. I know I need to come clean.

"Yeah, I did. I've wanted to for a while and I tried to ignore how I feel about you but I don't think I can anymore. I'm sorry, I don't want to make things awkward between us if you don't feel the same way," I say, once again blushing as I look at my feet. Do they do classes on how not to blush? I could really do with finding one.

He takes my crutches and places them to one side. He rests my hands on his hips so I can balance, our bodies almost flush together as he runs his hands up my arms.

"It was the hardest thing I've ever had to do, saying 'no' to you last night," he says, his voice low and rough as he pushes my hair behind my shoulders. The sensation makes my skin buzz with anticipation.

Yep, not breathing anymore. Where does the oxygen go?

Before I'm able to muster up some kind of response in the form of jumbled up nonsensical words, he explains, "I wanted to kiss you. I really, really wanted to. I've thought about it a lot and not just last night. This goes way beyond that but I just couldn't do it. You were out of it and I didn't want to risk you forgetting our first kiss. Or worse, remembering and regretting it." He absentmindedly plays with strands of my hair, making the hairs on my neck stand up on end. "You asked me why I stopped coming to your parties. Do you remember that girl I told you about? The one that was never available?"

"Yeah?" I say, remembering the conversation we had about her.

'"Did you love her?"' I had asked him.

'"Yeah, I've never stopped. Don't think I ever will."' he had said.

I'd told him she must have been an idiot not to want him.

"She's you," he says, taking me by surprise. "I realised how I felt about you when I went off to uni. That Christmas, when James and I came home, the smile you gave me when I walked in the room knocked me off my feet. Everything made sense to me then but you were going out with Philip. I thought, one day, you wouldn't be and then I could ask you out myself so I chose to distance myself from you until then. It was the hardest thing I ever did but I felt so guilty for feeling the way I did about my friends' girlfriend. I watched him propose to you a couple of years later and I knew, then, how much you really loved him. It would never come down to a choice between the two of us for you. I stopped coming around completely because I couldn't bear to see you be so happy with him and I hated feeling that way because I knew he was a great guy that deserved you.

"Then, he died and we nearly lost you, too. I missed him; I hated the fact that I couldn't be a friend to him because of my own vanity. I wanted to make things right with us but I'd pushed you so far away that, over time, we stopped being friends and it killed me. I would make up excuses to come see you at work and the only time I'd get a reaction from you was when I was winding you up so I kept doing it because even that little bit of attention felt like I was close to winning you over again."

"I didn't know. I just thought you enjoyed being a shithead." An uncontrollable grin spreads over my face and I can't seem to help myself as I wind my arms tighter around his waist, trying not to think about how lean and muscular his back is. "This is all so much to take in."

I'm trying to process everything he's said but it's hard when he is looking at me like this, like he's holding back, waiting to see my reaction.

"I wish you had told me."

"Do you still want me to kiss you, Maggs?" he asks, his voice low and breathless as one of my hands move to his chest, grabbing a handful of his shirt to steady myself.

Again, I forget how to breathe and words fail me so I just nod and hope that's enough of a response.

He cups my face and angles it to where he wants me before he lowers his mouth to meet mine.

It's everything I imagined it would be and more. Everything comes together in my mind, every word he's spoken that I didn't understand the context behind. Each argument we've had makes complete sense now.

Without removing his lips from mine, he lifts me up so my legs are around his waist and he can walk me backwards to sit me on top of the bar. This way, we're hidden where no-one can see us from the house, something we didn't think about when we started kissing in full view of everyone inside. Let's just hope no-one was looking out the window.

His hand slides up my bare thigh. His lips move to my jaw and down to my neck as I rest my head back against the wall, trying to take control of my breathing, unable to think about anything other than his touch or the feel of his hair in my hands or my fingers digging into the hard muscle of his shoulders.

I kiss him again in the hope that he'll see how much he means to me, that he'll see that I'm falling in love with him.

We could be kissing for 2 seconds or 2 hours - I really couldn't tell. He pulls his lips from mine and rests his forehead against mine. I let out an embarrassing whimper in protest.

I don't want to ever stop this.

"Unless you want James to walk in on us like this, we should really put a pin in it," he finally says, looking at me breathlessly. He strokes my cheek as the sounds I didn't hear before, of my brother and our friends, get closer. "Not that he would be surprised. He's probably guessed why I brought you out here alone, anyway, as much as he won't want to think about it."

"He told me how you felt about me earlier tonight. I didn't believe him," I say clearing my throat as he helps me to sit down on the wicker sofa, propping my foot up on a cushion on the stool and settling in beside me. I snuggle into his side and he kisses me gently through his own smile.

"To be fair, you were the only one I hadn't told. They're all sick of me banging on about how much I want you and me never having the guts to actually do anything about it," he says, confirming what James had said.

He kisses me one last time before everyone appears in the doorway of the summer house.

I don't think anyone realised what they interrupted out here, although they exchange looks between themselves when they notice that we're holding hands. My heart is racing and my mind is firmly in the gutter as I replay that kiss over and over. Thoughts of what could have happened if we weren't interrupted.

I commit everything to memory. How soft his lips are, how firm his shoulders are, how strong his hands felt on my thigh. I think about it as I hold his hand that hangs over my shoulder and rest my head on his chest.

My lips are still tingling and my heart speeds up when I think about how amazing our kiss was. There was always gossip at school from girls who had kissed him but you can tell by looking at his full, soft lips that he'd be great at it.

Every word he said to me is etched in my memory. I had no idea that his feelings went as far back as they did. I'd never noticed.

Guilt floods me as I remember why I didn't notice his feelings for me when I was younger. It was because of Philip. I was too busy loving him to notice my best friend.

***

As the night goes on, Jake deals with the whole situation much better than I do considering he is still able to hold a conversation with my brother without blurting out the fact we nearly set the summer house on fire with that kiss.

I, on the other hand, have barely said two words since our friends interrupted Jake and I a couple of hours ago nor have I really heard a word anyone has said and, yet, the conversation continues around me.

When Laura questioned my sudden silence, Jake stepped in and reeled off a dozen excuses like that I'm probably still tired from spending the night before in hospital and the painkillers I'm on and that he should probably take me home soon. Really, I'm replaying everything over and over in my head and wishing he would take me home sooner.

Eventually, I do manage to focus enough to hold a conversation but I'm fairly sure everyone can tell something is going on.

Mum calls us back to the house to sing *'Happy Birthday'* to James and dig into the delicious cake that Laura made. Everyone clears out of the summer house, leaving Jake to help me with my crutches.

"Will you stay with me tonight?" I ask. "I don't know if I

can function without help right now."

"I'll stay as long as you need me to," he says before kissing me again. "You need to stop looking at me like that, though or we'll never make it out of this shed."

"Mum will kill you if she hears you call it a shed."

"I know but she'd forgive me. After all, she forgave me for her vase," he says, making me laugh.

Around midnight, we finally say our goodbyes to our families and jump into our Uber. Everyone bought the excuse that the painkillers probably didn't help along with the alcohol I drank so they didn't fight us when we said we we're leaving before the party was done.

In reality, our moment in the summer house sobered me more than a large coffee and an ice-cold shower would have.

"Maggie, are you okay? You haven't said anything since we left your mum and dad's," he asks, looking worried as he helps me open the door to my flat.

I don't answer. Instead, I just close the door behind us, drop both crutches and launch myself into his arms. Luckily, he catches me otherwise it would have been really embarrassing and quite painful.

He hitches me up so my legs are wrapped around his waist, taking my weight, and he finally meets the urgency in my kiss. This kiss is fuelled by desire and is a bit more haphazard than the kiss we shared earlier but it's just as electrifying.

Less than 2 months ago, he was my annoying co-worker.

My brother's arrogant, egotistical best friend. Now, he's my lifeline, the person who keeps me sane, my business partner. Should I add potential boyfriend to that list? After his confessions earlier, I think it might be too late to refer to him as anything less.

Kissing becomes impossible as I try and unbutton his shirt while he holds me tightly to him. He finds the closest surface to put me down on which happens to be the breakfast bar that separates the kitchen and living room. He doesn't make any attempt to let me go.

"Maggs, are you sure you want to do this? I didn't come here expecting anything. We can take it slow," he says as I lose patience with his fiddly buttons and just rip his shirt right off. Buttons fly across the room. "Or not," he laughs.

I lose all train of thought as I stare down at his chest, toned and sleek with a sprinkle off dark chest hair. His body is just as gorgeous as it feels when it's pressed against me.

"What?" is all I can manage to ask, not making eye contact with him.

He raises my face to look at him. "I want you to know that I'm not here for a one-night thing. I've given it a lot of thought and I know you haven't but, if this is going to work, if we're going to do this and keep our company, then we have got to do it properly. I'm talking a real relationship so, if you're not ready for that, it's fine but you need to tell me. I've waited fourteen years for this and I'd wait another fourteen if it meant I got to keep you."

I thought I had seen every side of Jake but this side of him, his sensitivity, is new to me. He's laid everything out on the table for me: He's holding nothing back.

"Until a few hours ago, I had no idea that you felt this way. Every excuse I had for not taking a risk with you before now counted on you not wanting me. I don't know how to be a girlfriend and that worries me because I don't want to let you down if I'm terrible at it. I might not have realised how I truly felt about you until a few weeks ago but it doesn't mean it's any less of the truth."

"It's not like I have any idea what to do in a relationship either. We'll figure it out together. We don't have to label anything right away unless you want to. We can tell the world or keep it between us just as long as we have the same end goal."

"I want you, Jake. I want us. You're everything to me."

"You've got me, Maggie. You always will, I promise," he says, returning his lips to mine.

We discard his ruined shirt on the way to my bedroom and, as our kiss heats up again, I clumsily manage to pull my dress over my head.

He lowers me to my bed as I gaze into his eyes. I'm in disbelief that this is happening. He looks at me with so much love that it fills my heart, so much so that it finally feels whole again. Different but whole.

"What do we do about the boot?" I ask, earning a laugh from him.

"No idea. We'll add it to the list of things we need to figure

262

out," he says, laughing as he settles his weight away from my right leg, leaning down to kiss me again.

I know I'm ready for this. I'm ready to openly love him. I've never been so sure of anything because, when we're together, nothing else seems to matter but the two of us. He brings out the best parts of me, makes everything easier, everything brighter and better.

I know that, with Jake by my side, I'm exactly who I want to be.

CHAPTER FIFTEEN

"Maggie? What are you doing here?" Laura asks as I turn up at the bakery unexpectedly at 7am on Monday morning, clearly not dressed for work.

"What are you wearing?" she adds, taking in my mismatched yoga leggings and hoody. Trainer on one-foot, medical boot on the other. Barely keeping my shit together. My fingers tapping frantically against each other.

"I need a coffee," I say as my eyes fill with unshed tears. "Please."

She runs off to the coffee machine to get my usual order, not caring that I've interrupted rush hour as queues of people wait for their own morning coffees. I hobble behind the counter and into her office which is much more difficult when I don't have Jake to help me walk.

The waitresses don't bat an eyelid when she asks them to cover for her.

For the first time, I can't stop my fingers tapping on the arm of the sofa. Instead, I glare at my hands, betraying me by broadcasting my anxiety for the world to see.

When she's ready, she places the cup in front of me and I

take a long sip before quickly adding, "Laura, I shagged Jake."

She chokes and her coffee goes spluttering everywhere, including all over me.

"What? When? I knew something was going on, on Saturday night," she says triumphantly.

I grab a tissue from the box on her desk and dab myself down while she stares at me in part disbelief and part excitement like a kid on Christmas.

"Well, the first time was Saturday night when we left the party, the last time was about an hour ago before he went home to get ready for work. Honestly, didn't think you'd be surprised."

"I'm not surprised it happened; I'm surprised at how quickly you went from denying everything to jumping into his bed. He works fast does, that Jake. I have so many questions," she says excitedly. "Did you snog him in the summer house? Of course, you did. You had stubble rash all over your chin. Was it amazing?"

"Yeah, it was actually really cute then it turned really - I don't know – intense? Like, if you hadn't interrupted, I would have shagged him there and then. He helped me into my flat and I sort of jumped on him. I've spent the weekend getting shagged by the fittest bloke in London, possibly the world. It was the most incredible thing I've experienced in an awfully long time. It was perfect."

She looks down at my fingers, noticing my physical tell for the first time since I'd walked in.

"So, why are you here, looking like shit when you should be going to work to see your fantastic lover? Sharing an office doesn't look so bad now."

I wondered the same thing. Jake kissed me at the door and I told him I couldn't wait to see him. It was true, I hated that he had to leave to change for work; I hated that our weekend together was over and we had to go outside and exist around other people. I hated that I wouldn't be able to kiss him in the office because I chose to have a glass wall and it would be unprofessional to kiss in front of our entire company. I wanted to stay in our bubble forever and he left, thinking that we would be together again within the hour in our office.

We'd spoken at length about how we would make it work between us when there was so much at risk. How we planned to tell our families that they were right about us all along. How we thought people at work would react when they found out.

We were excited because, finally, after all this time, we were together and it was perfect.

All it took to ruin it all was one tiny moment.

As soon as I kissed him goodbye and closed the door behind him, something caught my eye. It was the picture of me and Philip on our wedding day that is hung by my door and it broke me. Grief poured out of me, seeming to stem from nowhere and everywhere at the same time. My chest felt like it had split in two, crippling guilt drowning me and my new-found happiness.

My therapist warned me this would happen, that, if I

continued to compartmentalise, it would all break out some time or another. She told me I had to deal with my grief to prevent this from happening. I didn't deal with anything. At least, I didn't until Jake showed me how to.

I think back to that night he held me as I sobbed in our office. He told me it was okay to be upset, that it was okay to miss Philip. He didn't judge me or invalidate my feelings. He just sat there and comforted me, loving me the whole time while I cried over another man.

I finally gain enough control to stop my fingers tapping.

"I sent a text to my assistant to say I was in too much pain with my foot and wouldn't be in today. I sent another to Jake and told him I had to take a few days off and that I'm sorry." I can't help the tears that now spill down my cheeks.

"Oh, Maggie, no," she says as she wraps her arms around me. "Don't do this to yourself."

"As soon as I closed the door behind him this morning, everything perfect that had happened this weekend felt like I was betraying him."

"You can't think like that," she says, taking my hands in hers, knowing that I wasn't talking about Jake anymore. "He would want you to be happy. He wouldn't want you to be alone and Jake has been so good for you these last six weeks. Look at how far you've come! If Philip could see you, he would be glad you've found love with Jake."

Ever since that night eight years ago, I've hidden my grief

from everyone, hiding the pain I've felt to make other people feel better. I did it to protect my parents, my in-laws, my friends, Laura but I can't hide this anymore.

I didn't want them to see how broken I was, how much pain I was in just by living, but there's no way around that anymore. I was broken and in pain. It hurt to exist without him and, during dark times, I didn't *want* to exist without him.

The tears flow heavier as I struggle to keep myself in check.

"Is that really what's going on here?" she asks me.

I have an urge to shut down, to put on my usual act and pretend that I'm perfectly fine but the way my best friend looks at me now lets me know that it's safe to let go.

So, I do.

"I have this recurring dream every night and it feels so real. I'm in the kitchen, I'm cooking dinner and Philip walks in. It looks like him but older, as though he's been ageing with me. He walks over to me, kisses my head and says *'Maggie, I'm here, it's going to be okay'*. Then, I wake up and it's not real and I lose him all over again. Every single day. Last night, I had a different dream. He told me that he loves me and that he's happy where he is now. Laura, those dreams were the only thing I had left of him. I'm starting to forget what it was like to be with him. I'm forgetting what his voice sounded like or what he smelled like. I'm scared I'll forget him completely if the dream doesn't come back tonight. I'm falling in love with Jake and I'm worried that it means I'll stop loving Philip."

Laura looks to me with her own tears falling down her cheeks. "I'm forgetting him, too, Maggie."

We sit on her little couch in her small office, crying together over our loss for the first time. Neither one of us were pretending to be okay because we aren't, we never have been. That's the first time I see the pain in her eyes reflecting the pain in mine because, for all the time I have been pretending to be strong for her, she's been doing the same for me.

"You need to tell this to Jake," she says eventually. "If you can't be with him, you need to tell him but I think that would be a mistake." I hold her hand, a silent thank you to show my appreciation for her. "For what it's worth, I don't think it's a case of loving Phillip or loving Jake. I think it's a case of loving them both for different reasons. I know Jake; he'll never hold your love for Philip against you. He loved him, too. I've never seen anyone as distraught as the way Jake was when he said goodbye to him that New Year's Day."

I know she's right - deep down, I do - but the irrational part of my brain makes me want to shut out the world and organise my brain again, to try and lock those boxes back up.

"Do you mind if I hide in your flat today? I just want to hide out so I can figure out what I'm going to do. I don't want Jake to know where I am."

"He'll want to know that you're safe. I think you at least owe him that. If you can't make that call, I can."

***

It turned out that hiding in Laura's flat was no better than being at home, even if she did bring me baked snacks every so often. Jake called me every hour, leaving voice messages that sound more and more desperate as they go on. Each time I heard his voice felt like a white-hot knife was being plunged into my heart. I ignored his calls, not knowing what I would say when I eventually spoke to him.

> Jake: Maggs, what's going on? Sasha said you're in a lot of pain. You never call in sick to work and I know you were fine a couple of hours ago so please just call me so we can talk about this.
> Jake: Maggie, it's me again. Laura called me. Please, call me back.
> Jake: I know you have your phone in your hand. I can see you're replying to emails. I'm begging you, just call me back.

Each voice message he left brought a fresh batch of tears because I had no idea where to begin explaining this all to him.

It's Thursday afternoon when there's a knock at my door. I look through the peep hole, half expecting to see Jake again but, instead, see the towering figure of my brother.

Jake only tried to come see me once, on Tuesday night. One of my neighbours must have let him in since he didn't ring my buzzer.

"Maggie, please talk to me," he pleaded with me through my door as I sat, listening on the other side. "We can work through whatever is going on. Trust me, all you have to do is just let me in."

I didn't.

Instead, I listened to him beg while I cried until my eyes dried up.

On Wednesday, I decided I would load up my laptop and work from home so I didn't look like I had completely abandoned my responsibilities. It helped me feel like I had some sort of control in my life.

Wednesday afternoon, Jake sent me flowers with a note saying, *'I'm still here when you're ready to talk about it'*.

Today, he hasn't tried speaking to me at all.

I sigh as I pull down the latch and open the door to let my brother in.

"Well, you look as shit as Jake."

"Thanks," I say sarcastically as I straighten my 'Do you even golf, bro' T-shirt and brush food crumbs off my leggings. "He told you?"

"Laura did, minus the sordid details, thankfully. I didn't need that imagery. I called over there last night to make sure he was okay."

"Oh?" is all I can muster up as I well up again.

"He's not, by the way. He's anything but okay but, since you jumped ship, he's had to pretend that everything is fine with work," he says, stabbing me in the heart with his words. I should have guessed he would be on Jakes side. He did warn me, after all. "What's going on with you? You were both so happy the other night. So, why are you sabotaging yourself?"

I can't bring myself to answer as I hobble back to my chair having finally mastered walking with one crutch.

"Come on, if you're not going to talk to him, at least talk to me."

"I made a vow, James, on my wedding day. I vowed to love him in life and death," I shout, burying my face in my hands.

He sighs as he takes a seat next to me in silence.

"I think you should read the letter."

"How do you know about that?"

"He told me about it the night before your wedding."

"How do you know I haven't?"

"Because, if you knew what he had written, you wouldn't be sat here like this. You'd be with Jake, living happily ever after."

"Do you know what it says?"

"Yeah, I do, but the words shouldn't come from me. You need to read the words he wrote to you. It's the only way you'll believe them."

"What if something happens and I lose Jake, too? I'd never recover from that," I say, voicing those worries for the first time.

I don't know what I would do if I had to go through that pain again.

"You walk out that door every day, knowing you could be hit by a bus. Doesn't stop you, though, does it?" He shrugs. I pull the letter out of the drawer in the coffee table in front of me and turn it over in my hands. "I'll leave you to it."

He stops as we reach the front door. "You should know, Philip knew. He knew that Jake was in love with you from the start and it ate Jake up how nice he was about it. You're forgetting they were close, too. It took Jake a long time to get over his feeling of betrayal and guilt. Why do you think it took so long for him to make a move?"

He gives me a long hug before I close the door behind him and hobble back to my spot on the sofa. I stare at the envelope for such a long period that it's getting dark by the time I look up again.

I decide I can't read the letter in this state so I grab a shower, taking extra time to blow dry my hair. Then, I take a slow walk to the corner shop and buy some Cadbury's chocolate fingers (Philips favourite) and a bottle of wine.

When I get home again, I change into my fluffiest pyjamas and slipper socks. I turn off the big light, instead switching on the warm light of the gaudy lamp in the corner that I was desperate to buy. It was the first thing we bought together for the home we planned on buying but never did. He hated it so much, said it was the ugliest thing he'd ever seen. He let me buy it anyway because I loved it so much.

I sit in the comfy chair with a candle lit and, finally, after more than eight years, I let my finger rip the top of the envelope and gently pull out the letter.

***

Taking a deep breath and another sip of wine, I unfold the pages and feel the tears sting as the familiar, messy handwriting is revealed

'It's just a letter,' I tell myself. Just. A. Letter.

My dearest Maggie,
If you're reading this, I'm so sorry.
I hope we've had a long and happy life, maybe have a few kids. Grandkids, too, if it's not asking for too much.
But, if not, if we didn't get that chance, I hope the time we had together was filled with love and happiness. I hope we got to make amazing memories that you treasure and I really hope you got rid of that hideous lamp.

I laugh out loud as I look fondly at my lamp.

I hope that made you smile. I know you loved that thing when we bought it so I imagine it's still stood proud in the corner of our living room for all to see.
It's no secret that I've loved you since the day I was born. There was never a time when I didn't want to marry you or

to spend my life with you so know I have no regrets in life and that everything is just how it was supposed to be.

If I were to die tomorrow (hopefully not, it would make a shit wedding), I sincerely hope you find happiness again and that you would live your life to the absolute fullest. Most of all, I hope that you will find the strength to love again and to grow your family because you deserve to be loved. Someone out there, maybe someone closer than you realise, deserves to be loved by you.

Speaking from experience, your love is the greatest gift you could ever give a person so, please, don't be afraid to love again.

> *I'll love you always,*
>
> *Philip x x x*

As I trace his name with my finger, the tears flow thick and fast. I read it repeatedly until the words are burned in my mind. Deep down, I knew what they would say. That's the kind of person Philip was: Selfless. Maybe I didn't want to accept that before because I didn't believe I deserved a second chance at love after having a love like him. I didn't think it was possible until Jake flipped everything on its side and showed me a new perspective.

All Philip wanted was for me to be happy. Did he know that I would eventually find my way back to Jake? James said he knew everything.

'Because you deserve to be loved and someone out there, maybe someone closer than you realise, deserves to be loved by

you.'

I was happy. So, so happy.

At least until three days ago when I pushed away the one person I wanted to hold close, the person who I can't imagine living without. I know one thing for certain: I need to get my shit together and deal with this once and for all.

A fresh batch of tears fall when I think about Jake and the mess I've made until I eventually cry myself to sleep in the chair.

CHAPTER SIXTEEN

"I was surprised to hear from you so soon after our last session, Maggie. It's only been seven weeks."

"I know I'm not usually forthcoming with you. I know I'm usually hard work and I am terribly sorry for that. Something has changed and I don't want to ruin it more than I already have." I pause as I notice my fingers tapping and they don't stop, no matter how hard I try.

Carol has been my therapist since the accident. At first, she would visit me in the hospital once a week while I was completing my rehabilitation. She would say it's recommended because recovery can be slow and this can affect people mentally but I don't think it was that. I think she came because I refused to speak to anyone but James for an entire week and they thought I was having a psychotic episode or something. I wasn't, I just didn't have anything to say to anyone else.

James told me what the grown-ups were saying. He'd listen in on their conversations for me because we both knew they wouldn't be honest with us. They still thought of us as kids even though we were in our twenties. Now, I know they were only trying to protect us but, when they started talking about sectioning me, I decided then was my time to speak again, as much as I didn't want to.

Eventually, I opened up, little by little. I researched trauma and grief online a lot. I knew exactly what to say to the questions she asked, I said exactly what they wanted to hear. My sessions dropped to once a month at home and then, eventually, a phone call once a year on the anniversary of Philip's death.

I don't know if anyone realised what I was doing. I didn't care as long as they thought I was doing okay.

I wasn't. I was good at hiding everything and I eventually convinced myself that the way I was living was normal.

It wasn't.

I've never been here before, in Carol's office. It reminds me of a day spa, all grey and white with fluffy cushions and plush carpets. Sounds of soothing wind instruments and breaking waves and calming, lavender diffusers are pumped into every room. It's a very welcoming experience. It feels like you're in a giant hug as soon as you walk through the door and even the reception area has the most comfortable chair you've ever sat on. I had to laugh at the cheesy positive affirmations covering the hallways. I suppose, to the less cynical, it might be a nice reminder that your life will not always be so shit.

Every time I engage in a conversation with Carol, I have a plan of what I will say with bullet points and lists to keep me on track. I always set a new goal, small enough that I can achieve it, big enough that it keeps her off my back for another year. This last year, it was to stop wearing my wedding rings. The year before, it was to go to the pub with my friends once a week.

Today is different. I called the meeting without really knowing why. Did I expect to find answers here? Am I looking for validation of the choice I know I have already made deep down?

Carol watches me through narrowed eyes as she pours me a chamomile tea, psychoanalysing me.

I feel terrible about how I've behaved to her over the years. I can't imagine I'm her favourite patient or anywhere close to that, really. I feel terrible about the money Mum and Dad have wasted on our yearly conversation that I give my bare minimum to. Maybe, if I'd at least tried to talk to her and deal with my issues, I wouldn't be in this mess now.

"Is that new?" she asks me, referring to my tapping.

"No," I move my hands to my lap, clutching them together tightly and desperately willing them to stop. "It's been a while since the last time it happened and, even then, it was infrequent. It's become a problem again this week. I try to pass it off as if I'm tapping out a beat or a song to try and hide it. I do it when I'm anxious. Right before a big meeting, before a party with lots of people or a time where I'm not fully prepared for something."

"And this is a time where you are unprepared?"

"Yes."

"Well, I am eager to see what you have to say when you are unscripted. Are you aware when you do it?"

"For the most part, yes."

"And you can stop it?"

"For the most part, yes."

"Tell me, what's changed since we last spoke?"

I know what she's doing. She's using the TED method we use when we're conducting market research. Tell me, explain to me, describe to me. It's a fantastic way to start a discussion, to get people to open up and give more than a yes or no answer like I have been known to do.

It's effective, too. Even though I know what she's doing, I want to open up to her, to spill every minor thought I've ever had. So I do just that.

"I took over my dad's company with Jake... he's my... let's just say it's complicated." I don't even know where to begin with Jake.

"Explain as best you can."

"We have a complex relationship. We were best friends growing up. He fell in love with me fourteen years ago and kept it a secret. I found out at the weekend."

"You say you *were* friends? Does that mean you're not anymore?"

"Not exactly. It's complicated."

"So you say. I'll try my best to keep up."

I think for a moment and start at the beginning.

"He went away for uni and he stopped being friends with me. It hurt, a lot. For years, I thought he didn't care enough about me to stay friends with me. I kept trying to get him to talk to me and I was persistent, no matter how much it hurt. That was until the accident, anyway. Before that night, I had tried so hard to get him to speak to me but he was always so cold and dismissive so I eventually gave up when I felt I had bigger problems than Jake Mills to deal with.

"My husband had died. I told myself I could care less about the boy that abandoned sixteen years of friendship in less than a millisecond. Over time, he warmed up again but, for me, it was too little too late so I did to him what he did to me: I shut him out. That was when I was twenty-two. I tolerated him no more than I had to at work.

"Then, seven weeks ago, we started working closer together. We had to share an office and we became friends again, best friends. It was like no time had passed, like we had always been this way."

"And you say he came clean about his feelings at the weekend. You've told me how you felt about Jake in the past but how do you feel about him now?"

"I'm in love with him. It's hard to say when I fell in love with him. Everything happened so fast, it was so intense. I just didn't think he could feel the same for me so I tried to lock it up in a box but, in the end, it wouldn't stick," I say as tears cascade down my cheeks. "We kissed and he said that, if it were going to go further, we would have to do it right. For the sake of our company, we had to be certain it was what we wanted. And, if I weren't sure, he'd wait for me until I knew either way. I was sure, I knew it was what I wanted."

I pause for a second to regain my composure.

"It was the first time I'd slept with anyone since Philip and I freaked out. It wasn't even because I had sex with Jake. It was because I knew I was falling in love with him and I thought that meant I wouldn't love Philip anymore. I was wrong."

"Do you regret what you did with Jake?"

"No! Of course not. I want nothing more than for us to be a normal couple."

"Explain to me... Why do you think you can't be a normal couple?"

I can't think of a valid reason that we shouldn't be together. Carol senses that I have nothing more to add so changes the subject.

"You said that your physical tics had come back this week. When did they become more manageable?"

"After I took my wedding rings off. It only happened a couple of times at the beginning, really, and I was able to stop them right away."

"Anything else notable happen around then?"

She smiles as the realisation hits me.

"Jake came back into my life."

She nods with a smile. "And what other differences in the rest of your behaviour or attitude have you noticed in the last seven weeks?"

"There have been many differences," I say, thinking of everything that's happened. "I'm not seeking approval or validation from everyone I meet. I'm not stressed at work anymore. I stopped working weekends and I spend time with Jake outside of work or with my other friends and my family, too. I leave the house and go places which is something I rarely did before other than to go to work or the supermarket, of course.

"For the first time in a long time, we had a girl's night to the West End which was something I would do once a month before the accident but wouldn't entertain the thought after. I went to a gig in a secret, basement nightclub and danced like I had no cares in the world. I played crazy golf with a bunch of people from work I barely knew and, instead of hiding in the corner to observe, I got involved. On Valentine's Day, I got drunk and fell off a stage while singing karaoke with Jake.

"I realised how much I have missed so, instead of just showing my face at the pub on a Friday night to please my friends, I'm there until closing with the rest of them."

"Let's journey back to why you closed yourself off in the first place. Tell me, why do you think you did that?"

"I was worried that I would have to pretend to be happy all the time. That I couldn't be sad that my husband had died. That I should be grateful I'm alive because everyone else told me I was so, so lucky. I know I'm lucky but that doesn't mean I can't be sad."

"And, when you spend time with Jake, how do you feel? Do you have to pretend to be happy?"

"Not at all. When I'm with Jake, I can talk about anything because there's no judgement. I can have a complete emotional breakdown in front of him and, instead of him telling me to talk to you about it like everyone else does, he listens and he talks with me. A lot of memories of growing up with Philip include Jake. He has memories of his own and we talk about that, too."

"So, tell me again. You say you love him, that you can talk to him and he's obviously helped you heal. What's stopping you from being together?"

"Absolutely nothing. I keep telling myself that I'm betraying Philip, that I made a vow, but Philip wrote me a letter. He told me to move on, to learn to love again. He told me that I might not realise it but the man I'm meant to be with is right in front of me. He knew that Jake loved me. That letter was him giving me his blessing. I think I'm just... I'm scared."

Carol smiles at me. "It's normal to be scared, Maggie. Grief is a powerful emotion. It can tear down even the strongest of people. The important thing is to acknowledge that feeling and to learn how to live with it. Losing a husband at such an early age will always leave a scar and this will be a battle you will face for the rest of your life. It's up to you who you choose to fight that battle alongside."

I check my watch. It's 7 PM, Friday evening.

"I have to go," I say, standing abruptly. "Thank you, Carol. For everything."

"Let me know how it pans out for you," she says with an

encouraging smile.

***

I race down the street to The George as quick as I can on my crutches (which isn't fast, at all). My heart is racing by the time I arrive, a mixture of adrenalin and nerves coursing through my veins.

It's not until I push through the doors and spot Jake across the crowded pub, sitting at our table and looking miserable, that I start to doubt myself. I have no idea what I'm going to say to him.

He stares into his almost empty pint glass, not listening to anything James is saying when my brother talks at him. I hate that I did that, that I put that look on his face.

What if I hurt him too much? Have I blown my chance with him? I slow my walk and weave through the crowd. No one has spotted me yet and they can't hear the clicking of my crutches over the sound of chatter.

When I get close enough, still out of their sight, I can make out their voices.

"I don't know how much more of this I can take, mate," I hear Jake say to my brother, his voice almost at breaking point.

"She just needs space. She'll come around, eventually."

"What if she doesn't? Can you call her or something? Ask how she is? Make sure she's okay. No-one has heard from her all day." My heart aches as he worries about me.

"Maybe you can talk to her yourself, after all," James nods towards me as I step into view.

"Maggie!" Jake says as his head whips around to face me. He looks as though he's too afraid to move, like I'm some baby deer he doesn't want to startle.

I've never seen him look like this before, so helpless. Torn between giving me a good telling off and not wanting to hurt me.

"Hi, Jake," I say pathetically.

"'Hi, Jake'? 'Hi. Jake'? That's it?" he says, finding his feet and closing the short distance between us.

He wraps his arms around me and pulls me in tighter than ever before. I tuck my head under his chin and revel in his warmth, knowing that, when we pull apart, I'm going to have to talk to him and I'll probably end up crying.

"I'm so angry at you, Maggie," he says loudly. His voice is full of emotion which doesn't help when I'm trying my best to keep my own shit together. "But I'm more relieved to see you."

He pulls back slightly so he can look down at me, clinging on to me as though he's still afraid I'll run away.

He looks like he's about to say something but he's interrupted by Cylvie who has now sat down with Helen and James at the table.

"I thought you were done with this floozy, Jake. What happened to not going back for seconds? That was your rule, right? It was the excuse you gave me, anyway," she slurs drunkenly.

"Excuse me?" I say, looking between her and Jake.

"What? You think you're the only person at this table who's screwed him?" she says with a smirk.

My blood turns to ice at the thought of them together.

"What are you talking about?" I don't look at Jake when I ask, "Is she telling the truth?"

"It was a really long time ago. It was a drunken mistake, I promise you."

I take a few steps to the side, needing to distance myself. I can't think straight when he's touching me.

"It wasn't-." I can't bring myself to ask him if it was the night we played pool, flirted all night and then he hung all over Cylvie the second she entered the pub.

"No, it was a really long time ago. If I could go back in time and tell myself not to even think about touching her, I would. I was hurting and thought it would make me feel better. It didn't."

"When was it?" I don't know why I wanted to know more details but I couldn't help myself.

"It was your wedding night," Cylvie says, taking an exaggerated sip of her martini.

I don't think I've hated anyone more than I do her in this moment. It takes all my strength not to slam my fist into her face but that's not me. I'm not a fighter and I'll not let her push me anymore that she already has.

James and Helen are still sat in our booth, looking as though they would rather be anywhere else but here right now and the look on Cylvie's face tells me he's telling the truth when he says, "She's just saying this to get in your head, Maggie. Believe me."

I know Jake has a past and I had accepted that but that doesn't mean I need to know about everyone he's been with, especially someone who has apparently inserted herself into our group.

"What are you getting out of this?" he yells at Cylvie, causing all of us except James to jump. "You think you're so much better than Maggie but you don't even come close."

"It's fine," I finally say, lacing my fingers through his, pulling him gently to my side again. I smile right at her. I trail a pattern on the back of his hand to calm him down and it works, he instantly relaxes. Cylvie isn't going to change my mind. I know what I want.

"Cylvie, we don't need your validation. I know how Jake feels about me and I know exactly what he thinks of you. So, yeah, maybe you do have a past with him but I'm not going to let that mess with our future."

He leans down to kiss my temple softly. "I should have told you weeks ago. I'm sorry I didn't."

"He'll get bored with you, eventually," Cylvie says. "You're too average. Bland, even. Jake is the kind of man that needs excitement."

I tighten my hold on his hand, urging him not to bite.

"If you weren't such a narcissist, you'd know that that isn't even slightly true." This time, it's James who has stepped in to defend us.

"How dare you call me a narcissist!" She looks to Helen for back up. "Are you going to let him speak to me like that?"

"Cylvie, James is right. You can't talk about my family like that. You shouldn't talk about anyone like that. Just because, once upon a time, you thought you laid a claim over Jake doesn't mean you can attack Maggie. If you got to know her, you would see exactly why he loves her. Why we all love her."

"Ugh, ever since you have been hanging around with these wretched people you have changed. And you've gotten fat," she spits.

I let out an audible gasp. Jake stands with his mouth hanging open and James clenches his jaw, balling his fists at her words. He looks like he's about to lash out at her. Helen beats him to it; her eyes darken and her delicate features harden.

"Yeah, well, that's what happens when you're pregnant," Helen says, stunning us all into silence. "And I know we've been friends for a long time, Cylvie, but that doesn't give you an excuse to be rude to me. I really don't need your toxic negativity so, if you can't be nice, you should leave."

James pulls Helen closer to him so her back is flush with his front and kisses her shoulder. "I knew you wouldn't keep it a secret for long." He laughs.

"You're pregnant?" I say, still stunned.

"Way to go, mate!" Jake says, hi-fiving James.

Helen nods with a wide smile. "We found out on Tuesday when my hangover from hell wouldn't disappear. Turns out... Morning sickness."

"Oh my god! You're pregnant! I'm so happy for you," I say again, reluctantly letting Jake's hand go so I can hug James and Helen. "Why didn't you tell me yesterday?" I add to my brother.

"Well, you were so miserable, I didn't want to rub salt in your wounds by telling you how happy we were."

I slap his arm playfully. "You're my brother. Doesn't matter how miserable I am, I'd always celebrate with you."

In the commotion, I didn't notice Laura, Harry and Simon arrive at the table, shrugging out of their coats.

"What did we miss? You're all celebrating and Cylvie just left looking like someone had pissed in her cornflakes," Harry says, making us all laugh again.

In the excitement of everything else, it seems we got a little distracted and I can feel Jake watching me. He has no idea what I came here to say.

As James and Helen tell the others about what happened, Jake's hand finds its way back to mine.

He nods to the door and leads me out to the empty beer garden. It's cold and wet but we're alone and that's all I care about right now. He wraps his scarf around me as an extra layer just like he did once before and I breathe in his scent like my life depends on it. I don't even care when he notices me doing it.

"You've got the hang of those crutches, I see," he says, smiling. The metal pole clangs as I lean it against our table. We sit facing each other, straddling the picnic bench, his knees resting on the outside of mine.

"Jake, I-" He cuts me off by bringing his lips gently to meet mine and it feels as natural as breathing.

Tears sting behind my closed eyes as he brings his hand up to cup my face. I've missed everything about him; his smile, his voice, his warmth. I want to savour this moment. I want to remember how I feel for the rest of my life, in his arms, exactly where I am supposed to be. So, I cling onto him, wanting to be as close as possible, terrified he'll vanish when I open my eyes again.

"Sorry, I... I just really needed that," he says, pulling away slightly, leaning his forehead against mine. We both know that, if our kiss deepens, there's a risk it will distract us from the conversation we need to have.

"I needed it, too," I say as I rub my fingertips along his stubble and into his hair.

We sit in silence for a minute, both of us relaxing more and more every time he strokes my hair or wipes a rogue tear from my cheek.

"I've got so much to say to you but I don't know where to start," I say, my voice barely above a whisper.

"Why don't you start by telling me if I'm going to like this conversation or if I should just kiss you again in the hopes it'll change your mind."

I laugh. "I hope you're going to be happy with what I've got to say and I hope you agree with me but I would still really like you to kiss me again."

He laughs as he tangles his fingers in my hair and softly kisses me again but, this time, it only lasts a second before he turns serious and makes a little more space between us.

"Tell me what happened, from the beginning."

I lower my hands to my lap and fight the urge to tap my fingers. He takes my hands in his like he knows I need the support, just like he did before our meeting.

"You should know, it was never a question of how I felt about you. I know how much I love you and I've known for a while, I just hadn't had the courage to admit it to myself and, if I'm completely honest, I always thought it was unrealistic that you'd feel the same about me.

"When you left on Monday morning, I closed the door and I saw the photo of Philip and me on our wedding day hanging on the wall and I felt so guilty, like I was betraying him. Every tiny bit of grief I'd ever experienced, that I'd locked away in some corner of my mind, came bursting out at once and I didn't know what to do. I wanted to talk to you about it, I wanted you to tell me that it was all okay but I didn't want to hurt you by crying over another man. Then, I thought about Philip, what would he say if he knew what happened between us; whether or not he would be okay with it and would he be happy for us? Happy that we finally found happiness with each other."

"I wish you had spoken to me instead of locking yourself away. I thought I'd lost everything... You're my best friend, my business partner and my... girlfriend?" he says, looking away from me, unsure.

I take a breath to steady my nerves. "I saw my therapist today. I *willingly* saw her for the first time. She would always say I shouldn't compartmentalise because, eventually, it would all build up and explode. She was right. Today, when I spoke to her, I discovered that there are no more boxes. I'm not clinging on to any 'what if's and I'm not holding myself back anymore. It's because of you. When everyone else told me that I should try harder to move on, you were different. You let me grieve him, you let me remember him with no judgement. We've not spoken about it but that day when you showed me your sketches, that was the day I finally started to accept everything. It just took me a while to get to where I am today."

I hand him the letter. "You should read this."

"What is it?"

"On the night before our wedding, Philip and I wrote each other letters to go with our wills. He had the idea when we saw it on TV and we did it, not thinking we'd ever need them. I've had it tucked away in my drawer this whole time. I knew I had to read it if I was going to let go of the past and find a future with you and that's what I want. I want to share my life with you. One day, maybe, get married and have a couple of kids but there was no way I could do it without letting go and, so, I read it. I finally was able to accept what happened."

He slowly takes in the words on the page before folding the paper back up and carefully placing it back in the envelope. "He was talking about you, wasn't he?"

Jake nods. He understands. "I know you still love him and miss him and that's okay because I wouldn't expect anything less. I know you'll still struggle some days because grief isn't always straight forward but I'll be right there with you. Please, don't push me away again."

I think back to what Carol said.

'It's up to you who you choose to fight that battle alongside'.

"I'm sorry I reacted so terribly. I promise, you'll always be the one I go to when things get too much. That's, if you'll still have me."

He doesn't say anything when he pulls me up onto his lap, holding me close. "I'm all in, Maggie. Are you?"

I nod as tears of happiness pool in my eyes. "I love you, Jake."

"I love you, too." He kisses me again and, this time, we don't hold back. Every emotion we have felt over the past week is poured into this one kiss and I know, in this moment, he has missed me just as much as I've missed him.

"Did you want to go back in or go home?" I ask, a little breathless.

"As much as it's been a really long week without you and

I'm quite desperate to get you home, I think we should go and celebrate with James and Helen. But, before we do, let's stay out here a little longer. I'm not ready to share you just yet."

And that's exactly what we do, we talk and we kiss until more people spill from the pub to the beer garden. Then, we join our friends again to celebrate the news that I'll be getting a niece or nephew this year.

As I stand at the bar with Jake, waiting for our drinks, I look back to our table. I smile fondly as I watch my friends laughing together. Helen and Laura are talking animatedly about something that makes Harry cringe. James and Simon are playing at the pool table where Simon wins for the first time ever and celebrates by running around the table with his shirt pulled over his head.

Jake turns to me and kisses me on the forehead.

We all know that life isn't easy. Sometimes, it's really hard and it seems like there is no way out but I know that, when times get tough again, all I have to do is look at the people around me to remind me of all I have to live for. The people I love, who love me and care about me enough to stand by my side through absolutely everything.

CHAPTER SEVENTEEN
Epilogue - Jake

I remember the exact moment I fell in love with Maggie Jones. The memory is as clear as if it happened just yesterday.

Our dads had always been best friends and business partners so I had known her my whole life but things changed for me when she was sixteen years old and I had come back to visit at Christmas, halfway through my first year at Leeds University. I wasn't far off nineteen and the little girl I left behind six months earlier wasn't such a little girl anymore. She was hardly recognisable. She'd had highlights which made her dirty blonde hair shine bright in the winter sunshine, she wore make-up and her braces had been removed, showing her perfect smile with no obstructions.

She wore her signature white sand shoes and a short, denim skirt that pulled in at her waist and flared out around her mid-thigh. Her olive skin and blonde hair styled in waves made her look like she belonged on a tropical beach somewhere not here in rainy Kingston.

She hadn't even looked at me yet and I knew I was in trouble. I was looking at her in a way I hadn't before and, if she had known exactly what teenage me was thinking, she'd probably think I was some kind of pervert.

Growing up, there were 5 of us: me, Maggie, James (Maggie's older brother) and the twins, Philip and Laura. We were inseparable, really. James and I even moved into the same student halls in Leeds while we studied. We hung out together all the time despite James and I being older.

The moment James and I walked through the door, her face lit up like a Christmas tree and completely shattered me inside. It was like I was seeing her for the first time. This new woman in front of me had stolen my heart and would never give it back. I didn't want it back, I just wanted her.

She ran over to us the second she saw her brother and threw her arms around him. I was jealous, I wanted her to have that reaction to me, for her to miss me that much, too. I was relieved when she turned to me and gave me her widest smile, wrapping her arms around my waist, leaning her head against my chest and holding me tightly. I had missed her and only then had I realised just how much.

There was a problem, though. Of course there was, nothing was ever straight forward when it came to my love life. Maggie and Philip had been going out for so long that no-one could even remember when they'd transitioned from friends to more. They were in love and it was so natural for them. There was no room for me in her life as anything more than her friend and the realisation was sobering.

She was only sixteen, though. Would her high school romance last? I would just have to wait and hope that, one day, I'd have my chance.

Philip was always so observant. He clocked the change in me the same time as I did.

"Are you in love with my girlfriend?" he asked me later in the night as we sipped on cheap Vodka in Maggie's parents' garden shed / bar.

"It doesn't make any difference, mate," I'd said sincerely. "She loves you and there's no way I'm getting in the way of that."

The rest of the Christmas break, I helped in our dads ad agency, sorting the post and making coffees. Basic things like that. Things to keep me busy and away from Maggie. To keep me out of trouble.

When we went back to Leeds and I tried to get her out of my head, I had a new girl every week, yet not one of them came close to filling the hole left in my chest by her absence.

I stopped all contact with Maggie, too. I stopped texting and emailing but thank god for My Space. I could still torture myself by looking at her pictures, seeing what she was doing and who with.

At first, she was mad at me for my unexplained radio silence. She would text and leave messages and demand I tell her what my problem was. No matter how upset she was, I couldn't tell her.

So, instead, I became a complete arsehole and she

eventually got the hint and stopped trying all together. I think I preferred it when she hated me out loud.

Two years later, I got a phone call the week before I came home from uni for Christmas. It was Philip, telling me his plans to propose at her parents' New Year's Eve party. He wanted to give me a heads up. He knew I still loved her. Why else would I cut them all out completely?

I'm glad James was still my friend but I don't think he ever found out the extent of how badly I had treated his little sister.

At the party, I avoided Maggie and she avoided me. Then I watched from the shadows as the girl I had been in love with for two years got engaged to the nicest person I knew. It hurt like hell so I got drunk on Jägerbombs that Philip had made and I threw up in her mum's favourite vase. That was the low point for me and the moment I realised I was waiting around for nothing.

I didn't go to any more parties after that.

I didn't go to the wedding 3 years later. Instead, I tried to repair my ego by spending the night with Helen's friend Cylvie. Something I came to regret immediately.

I didn't go to Philip's funeral 6 months after that either.

After uni, I moved back to London and took a job working at my dad's ad agency as a graphic designer and she was interning as a planning assistant while she studied at uni here in London. She would stop by my desk on her way to work every day to say good morning and ask me to come hang out with her, Philip and Laura again but I always said 'no'.

In the end, I started turning up to work 5 minutes after I knew she did just to avoid her.

Maggie and Philip had been married a little over six months when he died on New Year's Eve. He was 22. I didn't hear about the car accident until New Year's Day. I woke up hungover, maybe even still drunk, in some random girl's bed in Clapham - with little memory of how I got there - to my phone screeching at me. I had hundreds of missed calls from everyone. I had voice messages and texts but I hadn't seen them so, when I answered James' phone call, I was unprepared for the news.

"Maggie and Philip have been in an accident," he'd said. He was crying so I knew something bad had happened. "Philip didn't make it. Maggie..." he says, breaking off in a sob. My breathing was ragged, my temper frayed. I needed him to speed up. I needed to know she was alive, that she was fine. It didn't feel real. It's the closest thing I've had to feeling like an out of body experience and I could almost see myself taking the call, see the pain on my face.

"Tell me she's okay. I can't lose her, James. Tell me she's okay," I beg through my own tears as I jump out of this stranger's bed (who doesn't even stir) to find my clothes.

"We don't know, she's been placed in an induced coma. They keep saying big words and I don't know what they mean. She has a head injury and broken bones. Some of her ribs broke and her right lung has collapsed. They say she's critical, Jake."

"I'm on my way," I'd said, not bothering to wake the girl

I'd spent the night with and slamming the door behind me. Luckily, I wasn't far from the closest underground station so I ran the entire way.

I was a mess when I arrived at the hospital and I didn't care that people on the tube were looking at me with pity as I fought to control my tears. Could they tell my life was falling apart? Mum and Dad were there, waiting for me in the car park. I'd never seen my dad cry until that moment but, as he consoled my grief-stricken mother, he didn't even try to hide his own tears. I know Mum and Dad loved them both like they were their own children.

"We're waiting for the organ donation people to come and talk to Philip's parents. Would you like to say goodbye?" Mum asks. I just nod.

As I stand in the doorway to his room, Philip's mum meets my eyes. The pain of losing her child was evident and his dad sat with his head buried in his sons' side as he wept. Laura was sat alone in the corner; her eyes were red but she wasn't crying anymore. I go to her first and kneel in front of her. I take her hands in mine and rest my head on her knees.

We don't speak. Words aren't needed.

"Come on, Mum, Dad. Let's get a drink and let Jake say goodbye," she says, patting my head before they all left the room.

Philip was lying in bed and, looking at him, you would think he was just asleep. It's not until I sat on the bed next to my friend that I noticed the scratches on his arms and neck, presumably from the glass windshield shattering.

"I'm sorry. I'm sorry for pushing you all away. I'm sorry for being a shitty friend. I'm sorry for everything. I promise I'll look after Maggie; we'll make sure she's okay," I said as fresh tears fell.

I sat in silence, gripping Philip's hand, willing him to open his eyes as I waited for Laura and her parents to get back. I say my final goodbye.

I kissed his mum on the cheek, hugged his dad and squeezed Laura's shoulder. She surprised me by pulling me in close. I know I've hurt her, too, with my unexplained absence so it catches me off guard. I held her for a moment until she pulled away.

"Can you tell Maggie's mum and dad that Philip is about to be taken into surgery and they should come down now," she asked me and I nodded.

I took one last look at my friend before I exited the room.

As I got to Maggie's room, my heart beat harder in my chest than ever before. It was aching to see her, to see her alive and well. I wanted to see her face light up, the way it always does when she walks into a room, to see her beautiful grin and the sparkle in her hazel eyes.

As I'd reached for the door handle, I knew that's not what I'd see but I never expected to see her like this.

She was covered in bandages, tubes and sticky pads, her left arm already in a cast and an oxygen mask covering her pretty face. She was bruised and battered with dry blood matted in her golden hair. She was still beautiful.

I shared more hugs with her parents before I sent them down the corridor to say goodbye to Philip. James was sat on the floor at the foot of her bed.

"Mind if I stay? I've already said goodbye," James had asked me. I just nodded.

When I didn't think any more tears could possibly come, I looked at her tiny, damaged body. Each machine's beeping got louder and louder until I couldn't hear anything else and I completely broke down, sobbing into the blanket wrapped around her feet.

I felt James' hand on my back, trying to console me through his own pain while I incoherently begged her not to die.

After a while, I managed to get a hold of myself and sat with him on the floor, leaning my head against the foot of her bed.

We sat in silence for a little while, both of us thinking.

"How long have you been in love with my sister?" he'd asked as we sat side by side, legs stretched out in front of us.

"Five years, pretty much to the day," I said honestly.

"Explains a lot."

"I bet it does," I said, knowing that I've answered years of his questions that I'd managed to avoid until that moment.

"Does she know?"

I just shook my head. "Philip did, though."

Maggie was in a coma for 2 weeks while her body

repaired itself.

With 6 months of intense rehabilitation, she was back at work again and back to her normal self. At least, she was particularly good at pretending to be herself. I could tell, though. The sparkle that I loved most about her had gone.

Things between us were the worst they'd ever been. I'd spent years ignoring her, pushing away because I couldn't bear to see her so happy. Now, it was her turn to do it to me and she pushed me away every chance she got.

She couldn't even look at me anymore; it was like I didn't exist. The only time she would see me was when she was annoyed at me so I started annoying her on purpose. I'd flirt with her assistant and find any excuse to walk by her desk or hang my arm around her shoulder just so I could bait her into talking to me. Sometimes, she would bite; sometimes, she'd let her guard down and would lean into me sightly but, most times, she would just turn and walk away.

Eventually, Maggie found a way to at least tolerate me being around which was more than likely because she had to for us to work together as Heads of Departments.

I never told her how I felt about her, no matter how much James begged me to, but I continued to love her from a distance.

"You could make her happy, you know. She would make you happy, too, if she knew," he'd say but I had no intention of telling her how I felt; there was really no point when she hated me so much.

She still mourned the loss of her husband and a part of me felt like loving her openly would betray the memory of my friend. So, we carried on like that for years until, one day, our dads decided to retire and - lo and behold - they asked us to take over the company... Together.

Maggie wasn't happy about having to work alongside me any more than she was already doing and I didn't blame her but, with a little persuasion, she agreed to go along with it and I decided then that I wouldn't hide anything from her anymore. It was my mission to prove to her that I wasn't the horrible person I made myself out to be.

That was the start of our love story. I eventually figured out that I got the best response from her when I wasn't trying too hard to flirt with her or get her to bite. From there, it took six weeks of my charming personality and multiple dates with other men for her to realise that she, in fact, loved me, too.

One night, I'd rescued her from a terrible blind date that Laura set up at a rundown pub in the East End. I had an idea of what Laura had done when she sent me a text with the name of a pub and the time I should arrive.

By this point, the only person who didn't know how I felt about Maggie was Maggie herself and I had planned on telling her that night.

So, that's how our first *real* date began, when she burst through a fire door and into my arms. Maggie didn't even realise it was a date. That's on me since, for most of my adult life, I've been telling her I don't date, that I only pick-up random girls from bars... I'm fairly sure I asked her on the date, though, but I could be wrong. I'm often wrong but I try not to let Maggie realise that.

What I vividly remember is the trip we took to A&E after Maggie had an unfortunate karaoke accident, resulting in a broken foot and her getting so high on painkillers that she outright told the doctor how she felt about me, not realising I could hear every word. I took her home so I could care for her and she begged me to kiss her. Okay, she didn't beg but, in my head, it makes the fact I didn't kiss her even more of an achievement, especially since it's all I'd thought about doing for most of my life.

Although I'm a tough guy on the outside, I'm a bit of a romantic when it comes to Maggie. I wanted our first kiss to be special and I needed to know it was what she wanted when she was sober.

Instead, she slept in my arms and it was the best night's sleep I'd ever had.

I didn't have to wait long as we shared our first kiss the next night, surrounded by stars and fairy lights in the wooden summer house at the bottom of her mum and dad's garden.

I've had a lot of first kisses in my time, more than I'm proud to admit, but nothing compares to that night with Maggie. Like I say, I'd wanted to kiss her since I was 18 and had often pictured her face when I was hooking up with some other girl. Yeah, I'm not proud of that either but it's true, none the less. That night, as we hid from the rest of the party, I confessed that I was in love with her. I didn't tell her the full extent of how in love with her I was (I didn't want to completely freak her out) but I told her enough to show her I was being sincere which resulted in spending the rest of the weekend wrapped up in each other.

I knew it would be tough and I should have expected the mild freak out she had and her hiding away for a few days so she could address everything she was going through. In the end, we managed to work through it together.

It's the first time I've been completely happy in my life, where I'm not constantly pining for something else. Since the moment we got together, everything has gone right for us.

Loving her openly felt like a weight had been lifted from my shoulders and I could finally be honest with both of us. The years of angst and pain have finally paid off and she's mine and I'm hers. She's my best friend, my partner and my girlfriend, all in one beautiful and hilarious, tiny package.

Since that night, we've had an incredible year together. We've found our way as business owners; we even took some time off to visit her cousin in New York for a few days as we travelled down the East Coast. She moved into my flat just before Christmas, bringing her many cushions and candles which I didn't understand at first but, now, find quite comforting.

And that brings us to tonight, our first anniversary. Where better to bring her than back to our first date spot.

The steps of Potters Field Park, overlooking the Thames provide a beautifully romantic backdrop. Tower Bridge is illuminated, lights twinkle from the skyscrapers in the city and the Tower of London (which, granted, is less romantic what with all the beheadings and things) always looks good in the dark.

"I could look at this view every day for the rest of my life and not get bored," I say as we tuck into our vast array of food from the pop-up food market that sets up here throughout the year.

"We do, our office literally looks out at this exact view," she says sarcastically.

She looks so beautiful as she sits cross legged on our blanket. She's almost glowing and the twinkle in her eyes shines brightly.

"Yeah, I suppose," I say, non-committal.

"Are you going to tell me what's wrong?" she asks as I sit here like a bag of nerves. "You've been acting strange all day."

"Nothing is wrong," I answer, winding my fingers through her hair, kissing her softly. "I just can't believe it's been an entire year."

I go to top up her mug with champagne but it's still full. Meanwhile, I've drained two full cups as a bit of Dutch courage.

Get your shit together, man.

"Please, don't break my foot tonight," she says with a grin.

"Har-Har,"

"Would you like your gift?" she asks with an excited smile; she is practically bouncing on the spot.

"Can I give you mine first?" I ask. I need to do this before I really start freaking out.

"Sure," she says, smiling, the streetlight catching her face beautifully and sending the butterflies in my stomach mad. Why am I so nervous?

"Maggs, I just want to say something first," I say taking her hand and kissing it gently. "Never in a million years did I think I would be sat here with you on our first anniversary. You're the most beautiful woman inside and out I know I don't deserve you but, for some reason, you love me as much as I love you and that's the greatest gift I've ever gotten."

I stand up in front of her, pulling her up with me and I take out the small, velvet ring box that has been weighing my pocket down all evening.

I drop to one knee.

Recognition flashes across her face and tears fill her eyes as though she can't believe what's happening.

"Maggie Jones, will you marry me?" I say, presenting her with the teardrop diamond engagement ring I'd picked out 6 months ago.

"Yes, of course, I'll marry you. Oh, Jake, I love you so much!" she says through her tears as I slide the ring onto her finger. It's a perfect fit. She slides her arms around my neck, holding me tight and kisses me over and over again.

Relief washes over me. "God, I'm so glad you said 'yes'. Honestly, I've felt ill for weeks about it. I was terrified you'd say 'no'."

"Of course, I wasn't going to say 'no'. I had no idea you

were even thinking about this. I can't believe this. Does anyone else know you were going to do this?"

"Yeah, everyone knows," I say with a laugh. "I asked James to help pick the ring and, turns out, he was a terrible choice so I asked Laura and Helen to help, instead. I told my mum and dad, mainly to get advice on how to butter up your dad so he would give me his blessing. Then, when I asked your dad for his blessing, your mum walked in while I was basically sweating all over her carpet. She was the one I was most nervous about finding out my plan. I thought she might have accidentally let it slip on one of your drunken girls' nights out. Then, I asked Philip's mum and dad for their blessing which they were thrilled about. Then, I felt bad that everyone else knew except Harry and Simon so I told them the other night."

She laughs softly.

"Here," I say, handing her mug of champagne as we sit facing each other on the blanket again. "We're celebrating and, once we're finished here, we're heading to The George where everyone is waiting for us to celebrate. I promised we wouldn't be too late since James and Helen need to get baby Dale home."

"Let me give you my present first," she says, reaching into her bag.

"You've already given me the best present ever by saying 'yes'. Nothing will top that," I say, kissing her again.

"I think you'll find this one will," she smiles, tears still in her eyes as she hands me what looks like a long, rectangular jewellery box.

I flip it open but it's not jewellery inside. Looking back up at me is a pregnancy test. My mind goes blank for a moment as too many thoughts hit me at once.

"Are you? Is this real? You're pregnant?" I manage to force the words out.

She nods, smiling. I'm going to be a dad.

"We're due in October," she says, smiling at my stunned reaction.

She was right, this is the greatest gift I've ever received and I can't help the grin on my face as I stare at the two little, pink lines looking back up at me. For once in my life, I'm truly speechless.

Suppose that explains why she hasn't touched her champagne.

"I know we didn't plan to get pregnant but I've come to realise that the best things often aren't planned, like you and me."

"Maggs, we're going to be parents," I say, kissing her again through her tears of joy. "A wedding and a baby? We're going to be busy."

Suddenly, it hit's me. There's so much to plan. Why is she not buried deep in lists and excel spreadsheets?

"We need to buy a house. Maybe we can look at Kingston so we're closer to our parents? We'll need a bigger car. We'll need to buy furniture, pick a hospital, a wedding venue. Why aren't you in psychotic planning mode?"

"Jake," she says, holding her hand on the nape on my neck and kissing me to shut me up. "Let's start by telling everyone, shall we? I know you're supposed to wait until twelve weeks but I want to share this with people who mean the world to us. We'll just tell them to keep it quiet until we get the all clear from the scan," she says, softly taking my hand. "Then, tomorrow, we can go into planning mode together. Let's just enjoy tonight with the people we love."

I kiss her again, getting lost in the feel of her. She's always the voice of reason, one of the many things I love about her.

"I love you, Maggs. You, too, little bean," I say to her incredibly flat stomach which makes her cry even more.

As I hold my pregnant fiancée, I know I've found true happiness and, as I look to the stars twinkling above us, I know Philip would be happy for us, too.

The End.

<u>Acknowledgements</u>

Firstly, I'd like to thank my editor, Megan Georgia, from Megan Georgia Editing. The story wouldn't be what it is without your guidance and expertise!

Thank you to Ashley Santoro for my beautiful cover; it's amazing and finishes everything off perfectly.

To my husband, Adam, and my wonderful babies, Oliver and Hallie, for giving me the love and encouragement I needed to write this book.

A huge thank you to my mam, Dale, and dad, Kevin for being the best parents anyone could wish for. Especially Mam, for setting fire to the coffee table in the conservatory while making Flaming Sambucas and the countless girls' nights we enjoyed pre-lockdown!

A special mention to: my brother, Ben, my grandad, Raymond, my Auntie Kim and all of my Burgess cousins. I hope you like reading about Philip as much as I loved writing about him.

To my Lawson cousins, thank you for inspiring me with your incredible talents every single day.

A special mention to my besties, Jasmine, Miranda, Steph, Sarah and Sarah, for always being at the other end of a WhatsApp message.

To Melanie, Stephen, Abi, Ashley, Leigh, Alfie and Isla for being a perfect example of a loving family-in-law.

To Auntie Margaret, Auntie Angela, Helen, Trish, Dave, Angie and Brian. I hope you like your namesakes as much as I do.

Thank you to Melissa Morgan for being a great Beta Reader. I'm so glad we met on Bookstagram. Your support means the absolute world to me.

Finally, to you, my reader. Thank you for reading this story.

Whoever you are, whatever you're going through, remember: There's always a star shining in the sky for you.

About the Author

Ellie White was born and raised in Sunderland and is a proud Mackem!

She lives in Houghton-Le-Spring with her husband and two young children. She is a lover of chocolate, rom-coms, musicals and anything Disney.

If you've enjoyed this book please leave a kind review on Amazon, Goodreads or Instagram not forgetting to tag her! It doesn't have to be much, just a few words will do; it will make all the difference!

Follow her on Instagram @elliewhite_writes or search for her on Facebook to stay up to date with new releases!

You can also join in the conversation with Ellie by joining the Facebook Group 'Ellie White's VIP Book Club'.